Against Automation Mythologies

Inspired by Roland Barthes's practice of "semioclasm" in *Mythologies*, this book offers a "technoclasm"; a cultural critique of US narratives, discourses, images, and objects that have transformed the politics of automation into statements of fact about the "rise of the robots."

Treating automation as an ensemble of technologies and science fictions, this book foregrounds automation's ideologies, exaggerations, failures, and mystifications of the social value of human labor in order to question accepted and prolific automation mythologies. Jesse Ramirez offers a study of automation that recognizes automation as a technosocial project, that uses the tools of cultural studies and history to investigate the narratives and ideologies that often implicitly frame the automation debate, and that concretely and soberly assesses the technologies that have made the headlines. The case studies featured include some of the most widely cited and celebrated automatic technologies, such as the Baxter industrial robot, the self-driving car, and the Watson AI system.

An ideal resource for anyone interested in or studying emerging technology and society, automation, Marxian cultural theory, cultural studies, science fiction studies, and the cultural history of technology.

J. Jesse Ramírez is Assistant Professor of American Studies at University of St. Gallen, Switzerland. His research and scholarship explore American cultural, literary, and intellectual history, digital media and technologies, the cultural history of automation, science fiction and utopia, and ethnic studies. He is particularly interested in narratives regarding the future of technology and work.

Against Automation Mythologies

Business Science Fiction and the Ruse of the Robots

J. Jesse Ramírez

Routledge
Taylor & Francis Group

NEW YORK AND LONDON

First published 2021
by Routledge
52 Vanderbilt Avenue, New York, NY 10017

and by Routledge
2 Park Square, Milton Park, Abingdon, Oxon, OX14 4RN

Routledge is an imprint of the Taylor & Francis Group, an informa business

© 2021 J. Jesse Ramírez

Library of Congress Cataloging-in-Publication Data
A catalog record for this title has been requested

ISBN: 978-0-367-52014-4 (hbk)
ISBN: 978-0-367-52028-1 (pbk)
ISBN: 978-1-003-05608-9 (ebk)

Typeset in Times New Roman
by Deanta Global Publishing Services, Chennai, India

For my family

Contents

Acknowledgments

Portions of this book have appeared in the following publication:

"Race and Robots" © The American Studies Association. This article first appeared in *American Quarterly* 72, no. 1 (March 2020): 291–300. Published by Johns Hopkins University Press.

Introduction
On Technoclasm

Roland Barthes's *Mythologies* (1957) defines myth as the transformation of history into nature. Instead of concealing history below surface appearances, myth puts its objects on display and "purifies" them: "it makes them innocent, it gives them a natural and eternal justification, it gives them a clarity which is not that of an explanation but that of a statement of fact."[1] Myths *depoliticize*; they remove things from the contested domains of power and relocate them among life's naked truths. In 53 micro-essays—the full range of which has been available to the Anglophone world only since the last decade—Barthes details the workings of myth across French society, from wrestling to wine, "Garbo's Face" to "The New Citroën." The essays are guided by two principles: "no denunciation without its proper instrument of close analysis, no semiology which cannot ultimately be acknowledged as a *semioclasm*."[2] The principles enable Barthes to challenge meanings in objects that people commonly treat as being just so. Like all great works of politically engaged cultural studies, *Mythologies* expands the boundaries of meaning and activates the taken-for-granted as a site of analysis.

Though my scope is narrower than his, this book shares Barthes's project of closely and critically analyzing the mythological conversion of history into nature. Call it a work of "technoclasm," a set of essays in the breaking of technological myths. In the following, I focus on a constellation of US narratives, discourses, common sense, images, and objects that change the cultural politics of automation into statements of fact about the "rise of the robots" and "second machine age." The optimists prophesy that the latest digital technology will create many new jobs, the doomsayers claim that it will trigger a jobs apocalypse, but both sides presume that technology is a force of nature—objective, apolitical, inexorable, automatic. In one of the few essays on technology in *Mythologies*, Barthes observes that myth turns the Citroën DS into a sheer thing: "in this object there is easily a perfection and an absence of origin, a completion and a brilliance, a transformation of life into matter."[3] The same could be said of the self-driving car or the industrial robot Baxter. For automation myths reify cultural, social, and political processes so that technology appears to be a crystallization of "progress." If its origins in human practice are acknowledged at all, automation is usually attributed to the demiurgic genius of tech entrepreneurs. Because myth has automated how American culture imagines technosocial futures, we need a cultural studies approach to contemporary automation debates that refuses the beguiling simplicity of the question "Will robots take our jobs?" and instead foregrounds the value-laden cultural codes that stabilize the meanings and uses of contingent technical possibilities. As the technology historian David E. Nye observes, "the meaning of a tool is inseparable from the stories that surround it."[4]

In addition to Barthes, *Against Automation Mythologies* draws on four intellectual streams to press "quit" on the automation of automation. First, I begin with what Judy Wajcman describes as the founding principle of the historical and constructivist traditions in science and technology studies: "all technologies are inherently social in that they are designed, produced, used and governed by people."[5] Wajcman's axiom is concretized in my second stream, the five great cultural and social histories of automation in America: Ruth Schwartz Cowan's *More Work for Mother* (1983), David Noble's *Forces of Production* (1984), Shoshana Zuboff's *In the Age of the Smart Machine* (1988), Amy Sue Bix's *Inventing Ourselves Out of Jobs?* (2000), and Venus Green's *Race on the Line* (2001).[6] While these works do not exhaust the literature on automation, they are exemplary in showing how to de-automate history by situating automation in cultural narratives of progress, gendered and racialized divisions of labor, class struggles over authority in the workplace, ideologies of control, the politics of skill and knowledge, and debates about the limits of capitalist markets. Third, I draw on contemporary critiques of algorithmic bias, "weapons of math destruction," and the "black box society" that reveal how allegedly neutral digital technologies reproduce American society's racial, gender, and class hierarchies.[7]

Finally, and most importantly, *Against Automation Mythologies* is a work of science fiction studies. Spanning the entire cultural life of speculation, sf studies' objects range from genre sf—the popular media that are labeled or otherwise recognizable as "sci-fi"—to *science-fictionality*, a general orientation toward futurity that pervades discourses and practices beyond the specificities of mass-cultural genres. This book treats automation as sf in both senses. "Automation" names a collection of objects, systems, and practices and their imagined relations within an sf "megatext" of prospective and counterfactual discourses that encompass genre sf and the science-fictionality of American culture more broadly.[8]

There were two major waves of automation discourse in the twentieth-century United States: the Depression-era debates over mechanization

(1929–1940) and the hopes and anxieties of the short American Century (1945–1973), when the term "automation" was coined. (One could add briefer moments in the 1980s and early 1990s.) Since the Great Recession of 2008, we have been in a third period—the era of collaborative robots and AI, Watson and AlphaGo, Siri and Alexa, self-driving cars and smart homes. Today's dominant automation myths have narrativized these technologies in the form of what I call "business sf."

Extrapolating from the premise of capitalism's technological dynamism, today's leading prophets of automation foresee a civilization-changing redistribution of mental and manual labor through robots, artificial intelligences, and myriad other automated systems. The two main strands of business sf differ not in their assumptions but in their assessments of how smoothly society can adjust to the coming technological rupture. Utopian business sf foresees a technological revolution that will not simply restore economic growth but even push it far beyond pre-Recession levels. In the coming consumer paradise, everything from hamburgers to health care will be cheaper, more widely and instantaneously available, and higher quality. Transportation will be safer and more environmentally friendly. Cities will be liberated from traffic jams and, thanks to predictive policing, crime-free. We will have more leisure time, but work itself will become more satisfying because robots and smart software will take over the most monotonous or dangerous tasks, freeing us to focus on more interesting and valuable activities. Displaced workers will retrain and upskill. The entire system will be overseen by a benevolent corporate alliance of engineers, scientists, and capitalists, with governments providing socialized research funding and minimizing interference in privatized accumulation. In its most exulted form—the Singularity, or "the rapture for nerds"—utopian business sf foresees the transcendence of mortality itself. When, in contrast, dystopian business sf uses automation to explain the weakness of the post-Recession recovery and predicts that unemployment will only intensify as robots take over virtually all repetitive jobs, this discourse simply shows us the other side of the techno-deterministic coin. Dystopian business futurists share their counterparts' faith in relentless "innovation" but advocate for a limited basic income to ensure that everyone can consume his or her portion of the automated cornucopia under conditions of mass technological unemployment.[9]

This book is a first draft of the cultural history of business sf in the third era of American automation discourse. One of my central arguments is that just as the master's tools cannot dismantle the master's house, the master's technological stories cannot dismantle the master's futures. It is important to recognize the narrative and speculative nature of the dominant automation myths because their representations of automation are too often presumed to be statements of fact, not only by the mainstream media and general public, but even by some who want to develop counter-speculations. The search for systemic alternatives is exemplified by a remarkable new genre of socialist and communist speculation about automation that includes Paul Mason's *Postcapitalism* (2015), Nick Srnicek and Alex Williams's *Inventing the Future* (2015), Peter Frase's *Four Futures* (2016), and Aaron Bastani's *Fully Automated Luxury Communism* (2019).[10] While business sf is my object of critique, this genre of leftist speculation is the one to which I am most sympathetic and with which *Against Automation Mythologies* is in closest dialogue. I am especially sympathetic to the genre's hypothesis that automation is, or can become, a postcapitalist technology.[11] In one of his few remarks about the end of capitalism, Karl Marx claims that any *determinate* negation of capitalism will be "economically, morally, and intellectually, still stamped with the birthmarks of the old society from whose womb it emerges."[12] This economic, moral, and intellectual heritage is the dialectical counterpoint to our freedom, the side of history that we cannot choose. Because a postcapitalist future will inherit capitalist technologies—and because, barring the "common ruin of the contending classes,"[13] this future might have to be *more* technologically complex than capitalism—we should investigate the ulterior uses of such technologies now. Perhaps we will not find any; since technologies materialize past and present claims on futurity, there is no guarantee that we will discover postcapitalist uses for them. Many will have to be dismantled.[14]

However, while I engage with leftist utopian speculation in my final chapter, this book mostly takes a different approach. Instead of taking business sf at its word and projecting the alternative possibilities of the "rise of the robots," my aim is to convince you that contemporary automation is a ruse, a beguiling false impression. My primary concern is not to elucidate how automation perfects capitalism or inadvertently lays the technical foundations of postcapitalism, nor to adjudicate the technological unemployment debate. This sort of analysis is abundant, and I do not believe that we need more of it. Instead, my goal is to show that capitalism's technological promises are mystifying.

I call automation a ruse in order to make three points. For starters, the reference in my subtitle to Martin Ford's *Rise of the Robots: Technology and the Threat of a Jobless Future* (2015) indicates that my book is a rewriting not only of Ford's text, which I treat in more detail in Chapter 6, but also of the business sf that it epitomizes. Second, to call automation a ruse is to emphasize that some of the promised automatic technologies do not work. We are about a decade into the third era of automation discourse and we can already see that some of the revolutionary technologies are not so revolutionary after all. Many have failed; others will soon follow. In her powerful essay "The Automation Charade" (2018), Astra Taylor points out that "automated processes are often far less impressive than the puffery and propaganda surrounding them imply—and sometimes they are nowhere to be seen." Taylor sees much "fauxtomation" in automation.[15] Self-driving cars crash. "Killer" robots can hardly turn a doorknob. Reflecting on the poor performances at the DARPA Robotics Challenge, one journalist has coolly suggested the following defense against rampaging robots: "Shut the door behind you."[16]

But while demonstrating that a technology does not work is a forceful way to denaturalize automation, it only negates specific claims while remaining within business sf's paradigm of instrumentality, in which technologies are merely tools that either function well or do not. Whether a technology "works" depends on more than physics: it is a measure of the compatibility or "'fit' between devices and the interests and beliefs of the various social groups that influence the design process."[17] Thus, the third sense of the "ruse of the robots" is a critique of the "fit" between automation myths and capitalism's broader technosocial ideologies: when the social relations of technology are mediated by blind market forces and managed by capitalists and engineers, we all benefit from higher wages for more interesting work, enjoy more leisure time in which to satisfy our needs and desires through abundant and cheap commodities, and generally become wealthier, freer, and happier. This promise is as old as Adam Smith, who claimed that every sensible person immediately understands "how much labour is facilitated and abridged by the application of proper machinery," and as contemporary as Kevin Kelly, the cyber-utopian who thinks that once robots inevitably take our jobs, our natural response will be: "Wow, now that robots are doing my old job, my new job is much more fun and pays more!"[18]

Marx's retort in the first volume of *Capital* is to show that the Eden of capitalist consumerism—the "realm of Freedom, Equality, Property and Bentham"—rests on an inversion of technology's liberatory potential: "machinery in itself shortens the hours of labour," but "when employed by capital it lengthens them"; it "lightens labour, but when employed by capital it heightens its intensity." In addition to increasing the length, intensity, insecurity, and alienation of work, capitalist technology destroys nature; "all progress in capitalist agriculture is a progress in the art, not only of robbing the worker, but of robbing the soil."[19] For all these reasons, I share William Clare Roberts's conclusion that Marx's goal in *Capital* is to convince workers—and fellow socialists who are sympathetic to the idea of market freedom—that capitalism is a "thoroughgoing fraud, which will never deliver on the promise of less and more attractive labor," more leisure time, and overall human and environmental flourishing. The only way to stop capital's degradation of work and the earth is to organize and create a new society. If capitalist technology prepares its own demise, it does so not by giving postcapitalism a readymade technical apparatus but by giv[ing] to the laboring class a powerful *motive* to cooperate. [...] It does so, on the one hand, by destroying the laborers' capacity for going it alone, and, on the other, by creating disasters so immense in scale that only massive collective efforts could possibly address them.[20]

In light of the hegemony of business sf, labor's ongoing struggles, and climate change, Marx's debunking of capitalist technology should remain the touchstone of technosocial critique. This seems to me all the more important in the US context, since, as Bix demonstrates, our historical tendency has been to "enshrin[e] the gospel of workplace mechanization as progress, automation as destiny."[21] In other words, naming and critiquing the ruse of capital's automation is worthwhile in proportion to the ruse's social and ideological power. The more effectively automation myths convince us to surrender our rights to determine technosocial futures collectively and beyond the accumulation of capital—a ruse is a form of dispossession—the more urgently we need technoclasm. This holds true even for anxious business sf like Ford's, which preserves the main elements of capitalist technological determinism while attempting to rescue the system with a minimalist universal basic income.

To elaborate the stakes of this book's argument, it is useful to contrast my approach to another adjacent position. In *Inhuman Power: Artificial Intelligence and the Future of Capitalism* (2019), Nick Dyer-Witheford, Atle Mikkola Kjøsen, and James Steinhoff group left perspectives on automation into two camps, "maximizers" (Mason, Srnicek, and Williams, Bastani, Helen Hester) and "minimizers" (Taylor). While they rightly take the maximizing position to task for underestimating the difficulty of repurposing AI for socialism or communism, they uncharitably claim that automation skepticism simply flouts capital's long-standing use of automation to create surplus populations. Their critique of Taylor is especially pointed when they charge the minimizing position with being smug:

Capital always *has* made people and indeed entire populations "disposable." [...] Shrinking from that reality at the moment when a new instalment of corporate machinic power raises such disposability to a new level, and writing it all off as bluff and hype, may be reassuring, but it is unwise, sentimental and dangerously complacent.[22]

To be sure, the authors are correct to highlight capital's long history of using technology to deskill and dispossess workers. Aaron Benanav has argued convincingly that contemporary automation discourses' concern with technological unemployment is grounded in pervasive underemployment.[23] Is it true, though, that "a new instalment of corporate machinic power" is "rais[ing] such disposability to a new level"? This is the crux of the matter. Dyer-Witheford, Kjøsen, and Steinhoff assert the statement's veracity and fault Taylor for trivializing it, as if she were ignoring a concrete fact. Yet the future of automation is not a fact; it is an economic science fiction seeking to create facts. Although the authors are somewhat conflicted about sf, acknowledging its usefulness as a "machine for thinking" while worrying that they will be accused of falling prey to fantasy,[24] *Inhuman Power* is best read unapologetically as communist sf, a critical dystopian speculation that issues the terrible warning that AI-capitalism can render humans obsolete as a source of value—the apotheosis of value as an "automatic subject."[25] Looking centuries into the future, where humans must technologically augment themselves to compete with general AI, the authors imagine a nightmare scenario that outdoes even Orwell's vision of a boot eternally stamping a human face: "accepting individual death and species extinction would be the only alternative to working for a wage, 24/7, until the heat death of the universe."[26] *Inhuman Power* is a remarkable intervention in leftist speculation about automation because it remorselessly takes the inhumanism already at the core of capitalism to *one* of its logical conclusions.

What differentiates Dyer-Witheford, Kjøsen, and Steinhoff's view from this book's technoclasm is not that they take capital's history seriously while I am historically complacent. In fact, the skeptical view is the more historically grounded position, for it recognizes that as much as capitalists have dreamed of liberating value production from human workers, they have achieved this only in fits and starts and against great resistance. The history of dispossession is a long history of struggles and offers, at best, ambiguous empirical evidence for capital's coming *coup de grâce*. If AI-capital were to develop into fully autonomous general AI, breaking free of living labor and managers alike, this would constitute perhaps the single greatest rupture of human history, the ultimate "cunning of reason." To regard such an outcome as unlikely, even if some actors are inadvertently pursuing it, is not simply to rest assured that the status quo is fine or that "social struggles persist unchanged, regardless of new technologies."[27] Such hyperbole understates existing struggles that are difficult in their own right and implies that only the prospect of our utter defeat as a species is enough to galvanize critique.

Inhuman Power wants to invigorate critical thought by speculating about the most "deeply disturbing" possible futures of AI-capital,[28] whereas *Against Automation Mythologies* wants to invigorate critical thought by reminding us that our labor, both within and without the wage form, still produces and reproduces the social world. It is difficult to imagine how political actors could ever contest Dyer-Witheford, Kjøsen, and Steinhoff's dystopian scenario—or how they could ever trust themselves to forge a different world—without believing in the ineradicable social value of their labor, which is the basis of their right to choose for themselves what labors are worth delegating to automation. If I follow Taylor in "minimizing" automation dreams and nightmares, it is for the sake of *maximizing labor* against what is perhaps the most politically disempowering automation myth of all: that the world's laboring majority is inherently useless, and that their redundancy is a natural law of technological progress.

Business sf claims that capital can finally replace humans and that entrepreneurs and technology will soon be the sole sources of wealth. One way to marshal critical energies against this speculation is to extrapolate its full inhuman victory—to which I say, let the wolf's bane bloom among the hundred flowers of speculation. In the words of the great sf writer Kim Stanley Robinson: "If dystopia helps to scare us into working harder [...] then fine: dystopia."[29] My own strategy is to refuse to build postcapitalist imaginaries with business sf plots and to start instead from the premise that labor is the lover that capitalism cannot live with or without. What is more likely to happen *because it is already happening* is that automation will enmesh labor further into technosocial assemblages that make labor more controllable, exploited, precarious, mind-numbing, devalued, and invisible. To paraphrase and update Marx's assessment of labor in industrial England, "the land of machinery": we nowhere find a more shameless squandering of human labor for despicable purposes than in the United States, the land of automation.[30]

But who, exactly, is this "we"? While the "we" encompasses all laboring people, the stakes of automated value production come into especially sharp relief when seen from the perspective of gendered and racialized labor. This is the underpaid and stolen labor that constitutes the dark matter of the capitalist universe, the hidden and disavowed substance that holds the system together: housework and care, slavery and incarcerated labor, Mexican vegetable picking and traumatizing content moderation for Facebook.[31] Automation myths are trained on precisely this labor, mystifying it as a hurdle to technical progress when in fact it is automation's condition of possibility.[32] That is why digital assistants like Siri, Alexa, and Cortana are gendered female, why care robots are pitched as alternatives to the healthcare industry's predominantly immigrant and nonwhite female workforce, and why automation's prophets are predicting massive technological displacement especially in the logistics, service, sales, and office sectors, which are disproportionately Black, Latinx, Asian, and female.[33] As Neda Atanasoski and Kalindi Vora argue, the fantasy of automatic, disembodied value creation that frees the human for higher pursuits reproduces the racial and settler-colonial fantasy of expropriating labor, land, and wealth from subjects who stand outside the human.[34] Alex Rivera's Latinx sf film *Sleep Dealer* (2008) puts the point succinctly: "This is the American Dream. [...] All the work without the worker." Automation myths are not simply speculations about labor's technical disposability;

they are also dreams of purifying the body politic of gendered, racialized, and colonized others while separating value-creating labor from their bodies, presence, and political demands. Articulated predominantly (though not exclusively) by white male professionals, automation myths digitize capital's hoary patriarchal-racial-colonial fantasy of expulsion.[35] Those who have been living this nightmare do not need to imagine the day when automation becomes inhuman and labor vanishes—they already exist on the margins of the human; their labor and its social value have already been exploited, expropriated, and disguised. For an American working class that is more diverse than ever, technoclasm is a declaration of the right to exist as co-creators of the social world.

My starting point, then, is a present that is already dystopian, automated, and inhuman. Just as blockades and strikes build material power by disrupting circulation and withdrawing labor, respectively, technoclasm builds immaterial power by obstructing business sf's ideological flow and withdrawing credulity. For we must exit capital's automation dreams and nightmares in order to see alternative technosocial horizons more clearly.

Chapter Overview

The book's technoclasm proceeds in three parts. Part I contains essays that describe and critique the dominant mode of automation mythology in the post-Recession conjuncture, business sf. Chapter 1 situates technosocial speculations by managers and entrepreneurs in the "as if" structure of capitalist economic discourse and practice. I claim that business sf is not a description of the state of the art in automation but an attempt to influence future expectations. Focusing on Erik Brynjolfsson and Andrew McAfee's *The Second Machine Age*, Chapter 2 shows how business sf seeks to depoliticize the Great Recession and bend expectations toward a future that preserves and strengthens the hierarchies of "innovation." Part I ends with Chapter 3, "The Terminator, or The Automation Fetish," which argues that the killer cyborg annoys prophets of automation because it represents the domination at the core of business sf and market society.

Part II moves from speculations about automation's future to speculations about automation's history. More precisely, this section elucidates the ways in which business sf constructs a useable past. The myth of what I call the "original accumulation of automation," or simply "original automation," is an alternate history that serves as the go-to narrative for many advocates of automation as well as for progressive capitalists who worry about technological unemployment. The story is as follows: when American farmers lost their jobs to mechanization, they were "freed" to become factory workers; when factories were automated, service jobs were liberated. Now that automation is taking over service work, we can expect technology to vouchsafe new, better, and more freedom-enhancing jobs. Chapter 4 shows how original automation anachronistically posits capitalist social relations in the past in order to construct capitalism's history as a smooth succession of stages of freedom and progress. The chapter unpacks the myth's concept of "jobs" and demonstrates how it obscures the role of settler colonialism, race, gender, and class struggle in the transition from what sociologist James Parisot calls a "society with capitalism" to full-blown capitalist society. Chapter 5 claims that the whip and the cotton gin are just as central to the history of automation as farm mechanization and factories. The chapter argues that the lesson to draw from American history is that automation tends not toward ever-greater freedom but toward the technical perfection of slavery.

While the business sf writer and tech designer David Rose advocates for creating "enchanted objects,"[36] the essays in Part III are case studies that aim to *dis*enchant some of business sf's favorite automatic technologies. Focusing on automation in manufacturing, logistics, services, and social reproduction, the case studies are intended not as exhaustive but as representative examples of the dominant myths of the third era of automation discourse. Chapter 6 tells the history of Baxter and Sawyer, failed industrial robots that were supposed to revolutionize manufacturing and bring industrial jobs back to the United States. Rethink Robotics, the company that sold the robots from 2012 to 2018, went out of business not only because it misjudged the market for new industrial automation but also because late neoliberal capitalism is technologically stagnant—a state of affairs that is invisible to business sf's stage theories of progress. Chapter 7 investigates automation in Amazon warehouses and argues that Amazon's major technology is the algorithmic management system that surveils and disciplines workers, not its Kiva robots or delivery drones. Chapter 8 spotlights the ride-hailing company Uber and its attempts to build a self-driving taxi service. I argue that not only the self-driving car but Uber itself is a science fiction: the company is organized around the legal and technical speculation that the labor of human drivers does not exist. Chapter 9 is about the smart home and the gendered division of socially reproductive domestic labor. Against the hypothesis that the smart home will transform domestic labor into smooth, AI-mediated market transactions, the chapter suggests that the smart home perpetuates the servitude of mothers and housewives. Chapter 10 takes on the case for care robots: as the US population ages, there will be a massive shortage of caregivers. But the truth is that there is an abundance of people, largely female and immigrant, willing to do this work (especially if it were paid at its social value). Care robots thus exemplify how automation myths reify political choices about the social value of caregiving labor and about who counts as a full member of the American community. Finally, Chapter 11 deals with Watson, the natural language AI system that conquered the quiz show *Jeopardy!* I show how the attribution of human-level intelligence to Watson depends on the cultural hierarchies of middle-class and professional whiteness.

In my conclusion, I venture beyond the negative gestures of mythological critique and engage with contemporary leftist utopian speculation about automation and postcapitalism, in particular Bastani's *Fully Automated Luxury Communism*. Although Bastani adds an important political dimension to automation discourse that is largely missing in business sf, he also remains within the business sf paradigm. To develop an alternative to the master's stories about his tools, leftist utopian speculation needs to move laterally across business sf's extrapolative methods and reimagine the terms of technosocial dreaming.

Notes

1 Roland Barthes, *Mythologies*, complete ed., trans. Richard Howard and Annette Lavers (New York: Hill and Wang, 2012), 256.
2 Barthes, x.
3 Barthes, 169.
4 David E. Nye, *Technology Matters: Questions to Live With* (Cambridge, MA: MIT Press, 2006), 3.
5 Judy Wajcman, *Pressed for Time: The Acceleration of Life in Digital Capitalism* (Chicago, IL: University of Chicago Press, 2015), 27.
6 Ruth Schwartz Cowan, *More Work for Mother: The Ironies of Household Technology from the Open Hearth to the Microwave* (New York: Basic Books, 1983); David F. Noble, *Forces of Production: A Social History of Industrial Automation* (London: Transaction Publishers, 2011); Shoshana Zuboff, *In the Age of the Smart Machine: The Future of Work and Power* (New York: Basic Books, 1988); Amy Sue Bix, *Inventing Ourselves Out of Jobs? America's Debate over Technological Unemployment, 1929–1981* (Baltimore, MD: Johns Hopkins University Press, 2000); Venus Green, *Race on the Line: Gender, Labor, and Technology in the Bell System, 1880–1980* (Durham, NC: Duke University Press, 2001).
7 Ruha Benjamin, *Race After Technology: Abolitionist Tools for the New Jim Code* (New York: Polity, 2019); Cathy O'Neill, *Weapons of Math Destruction: How Big Data Increases Inequality and Threatens Democracy* (Harmondsworth, UK: Penguin, 2016); Meredith Broussard, *Artificial Unintelligence: How Computers Misunderstand the World* (Cambridge, MA: MIT Press, 2018); Frank Pasquale, *The Black Box Society: The Secret Algorithms that Control Money and Information* (Cambridge, MA: Harvard University Press, 2015).
8 Istvan Csicsery-Ronay defines science-fictionality as "an essential mode of imagining the horizons of possibility" in his *The Seven Beauties of Science Fiction* (Middletown, CT: Wesleyan University Press, 2008), 1. On the concept of megatext, see Sherryl Vint, *Science Fiction: A Guide for the Perplexed* (London: Bloomsbury, 2014), chap. 4.
9 The utopians include Erik Brynjolfsson and Andrew McAfee, *The Second Machine Age: Work, Progress, and Prosperity in a Time of Brilliant Technologies*

(Cambridge, MA: MIT Press, 2014) and Jerry Kaplan, *Humans Need Not Apply: A Guide to Wealth and Work in the Age of Artificial Intelligence* (New Haven, CT: Yale University Press, 2015). The dystopians include Martin Ford, *Rise of the Robots: Technology and the Threat of a Jobless Future* (New York: Basic Books, 2015) and Nicholas Carr, *The Glass Cage: How Our Computers Are Changing Us* (New York: Norton, 2014).

10 Paul Mason, *Postcapitalism: A Guide to Our Future* (Harmondsworth, UK: Penguin 2015); Nick Srnicek, and Alex Williams, *Inventing the Future: Postcapitalism and a World Without Work* (London: Verso, 2015); Peter Frase, *Four Futures: Life After Capitalism* (London: Verso, 2016); Aaron Bastani, *Fully Automated Luxury Communism* (London: Verso, 2019).

11 See my "Marcuse Among the Technocrats: America, Automation, and Postcapitalist Utopias, 1900–1941," *Amerikastudien/American Studies* 57, no.1 (2012): 31–50.

12 Karl Marx, "Critique of the Gotha Programme," in *Karl Marx, Frederick Engels: Collected Works*, vol. 24 (New York: International Publishers, 1989), 85.

13 Karl Marx, and Friedrich Engels, *Manifesto of the Communist Party: A Modern Edition* (London: Verso, 2016), 4.

14 Jasper Bernes has emerged as a major contemporary critic of the "reconfiguration thesis." See Jasper Bernes, "Logistics, Counterlogistics, and the Communist Prospect," *Endnotes* 3 (September 2013), https://endnotes.org.uk/issues/3/en/jasper-bernes-logistics-counterlogistics-and-the-communist-prospect; Jasper Bernes, "The Belly of the Revolution: Agriculture, Energy, and the Future of Communism," in *Materialism and the Critique of Energy*, eds. Brent Ryan Bellamy and Jeff Diamanti (Chicago, IL: MCM Publishing, 2018), 331–75.

15 Astra Taylor, "The Automation Charade," *Logic* 5, August 1, 2018, https://logicmag.io/failure/the-automation-charade/.

16 Daniela Hernandez, "How to Survive a Robot Apocalypse: Just Close the Door," *The Wall Street Journal*, November 10, 2017, www.wsj.com/articles/how-to-survive-a-robot-apocalypse-just-close-the-door-1510327719.

17 Andrew Feenberg, *Questioning Technology* (New York: Routledge, 1999), 79.

18 Adam Smith, *An Inquiry into the Nature and Causes of the Wealth of Nations*, vol. 1 (Indianapolis, IN: Liberty Classics, 1981), 19; Kevin Kelly, "Better Than Human: Why Robots Will—And Must—Take Our Jobs," *Wired*, December 24, 2012, www.wired.com/2012/12/ff-robots-will-take-our-jobs/.

19 Karl Marx, *Capital: A Critique of Political Economy*, vol. 1, trans. Ben Fowkes (Harmondsworth, UK: Penguin Classics, 1990), 280, 568–9, 638.

20 William Clare Roberts, *Marx's Inferno: The Political Theory of Capital* (Princeton, NJ: Princeton University Press, 2017), 172, 171, my emphasis. Mason and Bastani draw more on Marx's *Grundrisse* than *Capital*. For a comparison of the *Grundrisse*'s and *Capital*'s different takes on automation, see my "Marx vs. the Robots," in "Marx and the United States," eds. Dennis Büscher-Ulbrich and Marlon Lieber, special issue, *Amerikastudien/American Studies* 62, no. 4 (2017): 619–32. For a succinct summary of the diverging strands of Marxist technology studies, see Bernes, "Logistics, Counterlogistics, and the Communist Prospect," note 25.

21 Bix, *Inventing Ourselves*, 312.

22 Nick Dyer-Witheford, Atle Mikkola Kjøsen, and James Steinhoff, *Inhuman Power: Artificial Intelligence and the Future of Capitalism* (London: Pluto, 2019), 5.

23 Aaron Benanav, "Automation and the Future of Work—1," *New Left Review* 119 (September/October 2019): 5–38; Aaron Benanav, "Automation and the Future of Work—2," *New Left Review* 120 (November/December 2019): 117–46.

24 Dyer-Witheford, Kjøsen, and Steinhoff, *Inhuman Power*, 28.

25 Marx, *Capital*, 255.

26 Dyer-Witheford, Kjøsen, and Steinhoff, *Inhuman Power*, 159.

27 Dyer-Witheford, Kjøsen, and Steinhoff, 8.

28 Dyer-Witheford, Kjøsen, and Steinhoff, 8.

29 Kim Stanley Robinson, "Dystopias Now," *Commune* 1 (Fall 2018), https://communemag.com/dystopias-now/.

30 Marx, *Capital*, 517.

31 Casey Newton, "The Trauma Floor: The Secret Lives of Facebook Moderators in America," *The Verge*, February 25, 2019, www.theverge.com/2019/2/25/18229714/cognizant-facebook-content-moderator-interviews-trauma-working-conditions-arizona. See also Lilly Irani, "Justice for Data Janitors," review of *The Second Machine Age: Work, Progress, and Prosperity in a Time of Brilliant Technologies*, by Erik Brynjolfsson, and Andrew McAfee, *Public Books*, January 15, 2015, www.publicbooks.org/justice-for-data-janitors/.

32 Steve Lohr, "For Big-Data Scientists, 'Janitor Work' is Key Hurdle to Insights," *New York Times*, August 17, 2014, www.nytimes.com/2014/08/18/technology/for-big-data-scientists-hurdle-to-insights-is-janitor-work.html.

33 On gendered digital assistants, see Helen Hester, "Technically Female: Women, Machines, and Hyperemployment," *Salvage* 3 (April 2016), http://salvage.zone/in-print/technically-female-women-machines-and-hyperemployment/. For a gender and racial breakdown of the contemporary US working class by sector, see Kim Moody, *On New Terrain: How Capital is Reshaping the Battleground of Class War* (Chicago, IL: Haymarket Books, 2017), 40.

34 Neda Atanasoski, and Kalindi Vora, *Surrogate Humanity: Race, Robots, and the Politics of Technological Futures* (Durham, NC: Duke University Press, 2019). See also my "Race and Robots," *American Quarterly* 71, no. 2 (2020).

35 Saskia Sassen, *Expulsions: Brutality and Complexity in the Global Economy* (Cambridge, MA: Belknap Press of Harvard University Press, 2014). In addition to the literature on algorithmic racial bias cited above, see David Golumbia, "The Great White Robot God: Artificial General Intelligence and White Supremacy," *Medium*, January 21, 2019, https://medium.com/@davidgolumbia/the-great-white-robot-god-bea8e23943da; Shuja Haider, "The Darkness at the End of the Tunnel: Artificial Intelligence and Neoreaction," *Viewpoint Magazine*, March 28, 2017, www.viewpointmag.com/2017/03/28/the-darkness-at-the-end-of-the-tunnel-artificial-intelligence-and-neoreaction/.

36 David Rose, *Enchanted Objects: Design, Human Desire, and the Internet of Things* (New York: Scribner, 2014).

Part I
Business Science Fiction

1   Future Expectations

Some of the most widely read and cited treatises on contemporary automation are works of business science fiction—they just are not labeled as such. Martin Ford, author of *Rise of the Robots*, which was awarded Business Book of the Year by the *Financial Times* and *Forbes*, has a degree from UCLA's Anderson School of Management. Erik Brynjolfsson and Andrew McAfee, authors of *The Second Machine Age: Work, Progress, and Prosperity in a Time of Brilliant Technologies* (2014), are graduates of MIT's Sloan School of Management and Harvard Business School, respectively. Both currently work at Sloan and at the MIT Initiative on the Digital Economy. The computer scientist and "serial entrepreneur" Jerry Kaplan wrote the best-selling *Startup: A Silicon Valley Adventure* (1994) prior to publishing *Humans Need Not Apply: A Guide to Wealth and Work in the Age of Artificial Intelligence* (2015). While Nicholas Carr, author of *The Glass Cage: How Our Computers Are Changing Us* (2014), has a humanities education, his writing career took off while he was an editor of *Harvard Business Review* in the early 2000s.[1] I call these and similar authors business sf writers not only because of their educational and institutional locations in the professional-managerial-entrepreneurial class, but also because of their exaggeration of the present and future of "innovation." Before this term became a buzzword in the twentieth century, it was commonly associated with false prophecy. Business sf is one of the channels by which "the false-prophet innovator has been redeemed as the profit-making insight of the technological visionary."[2] In its most ideologically crystalline form, business sf seeks to educate desire for a more fully automated capitalism managed by a technocratic alliance of engineers, scientists, and entrepreneurs.[3]

Like writers of fictional utopias and dystopias, authors of business sf extrapolate current socioeconomic, political, and cultural processes; their futures are speculative models of the present. My point is not simply that writers of business sf are directly and indirectly influenced by genre sf. Of course they are. I mean that all capitalist economics is a kind of sf. When economists predict trends with statistical models, investors assess the future price of a commodity, entrepreneurs create business plans, banks issue loans, or consumers pretend that paper, metal, and digits on a screen are money, and that their purchases will satisfy their needs and desires, they all act *as if* the objects and conditions of their practices were real and knowable, despite the fact that such objects and conditions are contingent on unobservable qualities and an uncertain future. The economic sociologist Jens Beckert explains that

> expectations of the unforeseeable future inhabit the mind not as fore-knowledge, but as contingent imaginaries. Actors, motivated by an imagined future state, organize their activities based on this mental representation and the emotions associated with it. Expectations under conditions of uncertainty and ascribed symbolic meanings may be seen as a kind of *pretending*.[4]

In other words, when business sf describes the future of automation, it channels the make-believe that fundamentally orients economic thought and practice in a society enthralled by the market's structural unpredictability.

However, unlike most sf writers, the authorities in the contemporary automation debate benefit from the sober respect that American society routinely pays to visionary businessmen. Their books are not marketed or read as fiction. Amazon lists *Rise of the Robots* and *The Second Machine Age* as top sellers in "Industrial Technology" and "Robotics." Deference to business expertise is one reason many Americans voted for Donald Trump in 2016—they believed that only a "successful businessman" can run the country—and helps to explain why the vast majority of Americans accept the story that business sf is telling. According to a recent Pew poll, 82% think automation will take over much of the work currently done by humans.[5] These Americans do not recognize business prognoses of the automated future as fiction, but as eyewitness reports from the "business world," which, like an upside-down version of Plato's realm of immaterial forms, is the bedrock reality of cash and calculation that underlies ordinary life.

The usual business of genre sf is to entertain, to incite wonder, or to provide critical distance from the present by symbolically transforming it into the past of a hypothetical future.[6] Even the most politically conscious genre sf has a highly mediated relationship to action. In contrast, business sf claims to describe what is the case and starts from the premise of genre sf's transcendence *in order to influence future expectations*. Brynjolfsson and McAfee constantly remind their readers that the technologies they describe *used* to be "the stuff of science fiction" and have since become "business reality."[7] Admitting to pretending would jeopardize their stature as authorities and their ability to elicit actions such as private and government investment in automation. Glossing Pierre Bourdieu, Beckert observes that "the nonfictional character of assertions is an '*illusio*' to be maintained in the economic field; the belief (*croyance*) that assessments of future states of the world are accurate anticipations of the future present must be protected to maintain actors' confidence."[8]

It is a truism among genre sf authors and scholars that representations of the future are really about the time in which they were created, which includes that historical moment's understanding of its past. To read sf futures as sheer prediction is to turn a blind eye to the worlds that ground speculation and against which speculation produces meaning for historically situated interpretive communities. Yet this blindness is precisely what business sf's "*illusio*" wants to maintain in order to keep its speculations circulating as fluidly and widely as the capital that it seeks to attract. To unlock the sf side of automation discourse, to recognize business sf as a political and socially interested intervention in the present and past—this is the work of the following chapters.

Notes

1 Kaplan's website (jerrykaplan.com) describes the author as a "serial entrepreneur." Raymond Kurzweil, author of *The Age of Spiritual Machines: When Computers Exceed Human Intelligence* (1999) is business sf's most radically speculative writer. Note how Brynjolfsson and McAfee riff on Kurzweil's title while subtly turning his quasi-religious "spiritual machines" into the more secular sounding "brilliant technologies."

2 John Patrick Leary, "The Innovation Cult," *Jacobin*, April 16, 2019, www.jacobinmag.com/2019/04/innovation-language-of-capitalism-ideology-disruption. See also John Patrick Leary, *Keywords: The New Language of Capitalism* (Chicago, IL: Haymarket Books, 2019).

3 In Marxist sf studies, the education of desire is one of the principal functions of utopia. See Ruth Levitas, *The Concept of Utopia* (Oxford: Peter Lang, 2010).

4 Jens Beckert, *Imagined Futures: Fictional Expectations and Capitalist Dynamics* (Cambridge, MA: Harvard University Press, 2016), 9–10.

5 A. W. Geiger, "How Americans See Automation and the Workplace in 7 Charts," *Pew Research Center*, April 8, 2019, www.pewresearch.org/fact-tank/2019/04/08/how-americans-see-automation-and-the-workplace-in-7-charts/.

6 Fredric Jameson, *Archaeologies of the Future: The Desire Called Utopia and Other Science Fictions* (London: Verso, 2005), 281–95.

7 Brynjolfsson and McAfee, *The Second Machine Age*, 11, 12, 19, 48.

8 Beckert, *Imagined Futures*, 73.

2   "Harbingers of the Robot Age"

Erik Brynjolfsson and Andrew McAfee are two of our era's most influential automation mythologists. In the words of *Politico*, they are the "Harbingers of the Robot Age."[1]

In 2013, Brynjolfsson was invited to a panel organized by the Obama Administration's Council of Advisors on Science and Technology. *The Second Machine Age* was then prominently cited in the Obama Administration's report "Artificial Intelligence, Automation, and the Economy" (2016).[2] The book's appeal is due to the simplicity and optimism of its story: everything is about to get much better. We are on the verge of a "second machine age." The original machine age was continuous with the Industrial Revolution, the first epoch in which technology was the prime mover of progress. The second machine age will be another radical transformation of human history, this time driven by digital technologies like self-driving cars, IBM's Watson, and the industrial robot Baxter. These "brilliant technologies" have performed tasks that were once widely considered impossible for computers and have brought civilization to an "inflection point" after which further technological change, propelled by Moore's Law, will unfold at an exponential and unfathomable pace.[3] There will be bumps along the way, such as rising income inequality and unemployment, but with a few relatively minor reforms, we can look forward to a more productive and wealthy future. Add some concerns about diversity in the tech industry and one has described Obama's own position on the future of automation, which was published in business sf's house organ, *Wired*.[4]

Much of *The Second Machine Age* is a reprise of Brynjolfsson and McAfee's first book, *Race Against the Machine: How the Digital Revolution is Accelerating Innovation, Driving Productivity, and Irreversibly Transforming Employment and the Economy* (2011). While the earlier book is also optimistic, it is somewhat more alarmist than *The Second Machine Age*. "More Jobs Predicted for Machines, Not People," announced the *New York Times*'s review.[5] After all, *Race Against the Machine* was written in the wake of the Great Recession and appeared during the height of Occupy Wall Street and the revolt of the 99%. Amid a jobless recovery and popular anti-capitalist movements, the authors must have found it difficult to write about "a cornucopia of innovation," which is how McAfee has described the book's original focus.[6] Given this political context, Brynjolfsson and McAfee's analysis can be seen as ideological triage, an attempt to shift attention from Wall Street and class struggle to a more impersonal, neutral-sounding, and thus depoliticized target: digital technology. In fact, since, as they claim, technological innovation is more robust than ever before, the apparent signs of capitalism's corruption are effects of the system's strength. Echoing William F. Ogburn's old cultural lag thesis, Brynjolfsson and McAfee posit that the reason for joblessness and economic inequality is low- and middle-skill workers' inability to keep pace with ever-accelerating automation: "Our technologies are racing ahead but many of our skills and organizations are lagging behind."[7] The difference between *Race Against the Machine* and *The Second Machine Age* is that the latter no longer begins with the Great Recession and instead foregrounds the "cornucopia" narrative that the authors originally wanted to write. Published three years after Occupy's eviction from Zuccotti Park, *The Second Machine Age* does not feel the need to turn capitalist crisis on its head. The book effectively announces that the revolt is over and that a postcapitalist world is neither possible nor necessary. For this is a tale of capitalism's comeback, its unstoppable technological dynamism, and its utopian future. The point is not to explain or assuage the Great Recession but to erase it from memory.

When *The Second Machine Age* explains the ultimate causes of technological change, it wavers between technological determinism and the ideologies of innovation. The authors repeat their thesis from *Race Against the Machine* that the cause of economic equality is not political but technical:

> In the past couple of decades, we've seen changes in tax policy, greater overseas competition, ongoing government waste, and Wall Street shenanigans. But when we look at the data and research, we conclude that none of these are the primary driver of growing inequality. Instead, the main driver is exponential, digital, and combinatorial change in the technology that undergirds our economic system.[8]

But if technology is the culprit, Brynjolfsson and McAfee caution against trying to stop it. Or more precisely, *because* the problem is technological it is pointless to *want* to stop it: "We need to let the technologies of the second machine age do their work and find ways to deal with the challenges they will bring with them."[9] Technology acts, people react. Technology's work is secure, so people's work must become flexible. Such rhetoric pacifies future expectations and generates a sense of inevitability. It is unfair that digital technologies disproportionately enrich the 1%, but that is just what digital technologies do.

Yet when the authors explain that Moore's Law virtually guarantees that the computation behind many forms of automation will become mind-bogglingly fast in the near future, they concede that Moore's Law is not actually a law. Instead, they define it as "a statement about the work of the computer industry's engineers and scientists; it's an observation about how constant and successful their efforts have been."[10] According to Intel's website, co-founder Gordon Moore proposed that "The number of transistors incorporated in a chip will approximately double every 24 months." The quotation is not quite accurate. Historian of science and technology Cyrus C. M. Mody points out that Moore's original conjecture was that it takes about 12, not 24, months for transistors to double. More importantly, Moore was referring specifically to "the density of circuit components per unit area that it is most *economically profitable* for commercial, high-volume manufacturers to cram onto silicon."[11] In other words, Moore's Law is business sf; given its centrality to contemporary automation myths, Moore's Law can be understood as *the* business sf, the genre's ur-myth. Moore speculated about the conditions for the most *profitable* production of computer chips. To treat Moore's Law as a natural law is simply to naturalize profit-seeking. But the fact that subsequent chip production has mostly hewed to the line of Moore's extrapolation shows that just because economics is make-believe, it does not follow that economic fictions are inconsequential. Money is fictional, but having it or not is often the difference between security and suffering, even life and death. Fictions accrue material power when they are embedded in shared language, thought, practice, and institutions. This is roughly what Mody means when he claims that Moore's Law is "a 'social fact' that is continually made into empirical fact by actors' perception of Moore's Law as empirical fact."[12] By behaving *as if* Moore's speculation were a statement of fact, actors in the semiconductor industry coordinate a complex division of labor and establish benchmarks for financial gain.

By reformulating Moore's Law as a description of the activities of corporate engineers and scientists, Brynjolfsson and McAfee indirectly acknowledge that Moore's Law is a social fact. But if that concept has the potential to expose the fictionality of economic principles, and perhaps even to cast doubt on the certainty of automation's future advance, in Brynjolfsson and McAfee's hands it is a celebration of the difference between high-skilled, creative professionals and the "lagging" low- and middle-skilled masses. Transistors and computer speed have been doubling at a steady rate because whenever engineers have encountered limits, they have solved the problem with "brilliant tinkering."[13] If this sounds like it contradicts Brynjolfsson and McAfee's view that technology drives history, it can also be understood as a slip of the tongue that reveals that their technological determinism is ultimately a cover for capitalist determinism.

In a mostly positive review of *The Second Machine Age*, Frank Pasquale faults the authors' "refusal to name the responsible parties *running* the machines."[14] But the answer is clear. In a blog post about his participation in the World Economic Forum in Davos, Switzerland, McAfee elucidates the groupthink at the ideological core of *The Second Machine Age*. McAfee says he associates mainly with "technologists, entrepreneurs, businesspeople, and economists at American universities," and that they all believe that the following capitalist maxims are beyond reasonable debate: "creative destruction is good news," "markets allocate better than bureaucrats do," "there is such a thing as too much regulation," "business is not the enemy," "the state can't provide jobs to everybody." Astonishingly, McAfee claims that his fellow panelists at Davos were not sufficiently committed to American free-market ideology: "they seemed to believe much more strongly in government planning, programs, and protections as the best way to ensure good jobs and wages."[15] If one regards the technocrats at the world's preeminent neoliberal gathering as too social-democratic, this is a rather clear sign that one's worldview is the gold standard of market fundamentalism.

To answer Pasquale's question: tinkerers, scientists, and the businesses that finance and employ them are running the machines. The "brilliant" technologies in the book's subtitle reflect the brilliance of tech entrepreneurs. When Brynjolfsson and McAfee advise against trying to stop the second machine age, they mean that we should not disturb their preferred alliance of engineers, scientists, and capitalists, nor the market forces that mediate these actors' influence over automation's past, present, and future. Since "innovators" have given us the wonders of automation, we should trust in them to manage its negative effects. In their chapter on long-term policy recommendations, the authors underscore that "the best solutions—probably, in fact, the only real solutions—to the labor force challenges that will arise in the future will come from markets and capitalism, and from the technology-enabled creations of innovators and entrepreneurs."[16] Here, business sf's extrapolations interlock with what the economist Mariana Mazzucato characterizes as narratives of "wealth creation," which identify entrepreneurs as the most productive, imaginative, risk-taking, and virtuous members of society. By strengthening the fiction that "wealth creators" grow the economic pie while others only cut it up and distribute it, these narratives help to convince us that elites' authority and money are natural, deserved, and beneficial to everyone (as long as we leave this authority and most of the money untouched).[17] "We champion entrepreneurship," Brynjolfsson and McAfee explain, "because entrepreneurship is the best way to create jobs and opportunity." "Ambitious entrepreneurs are best at this, not well-meaning government leaders or visionary academics."[18] No wonder that Rodney Brooks, founder of iRobot and former CEO of Rethink Robotics, and Hal Varian, Google's chief economist, wrote glowing blurbs for Brynjolfsson and McAfee's book. For they share the authors' vision of a technocratic future in which managers and their allies are left alone to design a world that enriches them more automatically—a world in which their fictions take on a more material form.

To be sure, Brynjolfsson and McAfee are not pure technochauvinists.[19] They are concerned that while automation increases overall "bounty," it also encourages "'winner-take-all' markets" and exacerbates "spread," "the gap between the superstars in a field and everyone else."[20] The authors are also refreshingly skeptical of the market-fundamentalist argument that technological unemployment, if it happens at all, is always local and temporary. They encourage engineers to design labor-augmenting (as opposed to labor-displacing) technologies, call for more spending on education, and even briefly propose raising marginal tax rates on the super-wealthy.

However, for all their attempts to stimulate the reader's imagination, the future toward which Brynjolfsson and McAfee want to bend our enthusiasm is a remarkably unimaginative defense of the present. The business fantastic is ultimately only a slightly embellished form of capitalist realism. Brynjolfsson and McAfee reject the attempt to "come up with fundamental alternatives to capitalism."[21] Agreeing with Voltaire's view that "work saves a man from three great evils: boredom, vice, and need," they assure us that no matter how much labor automation might save, the capitalist work ethic must always rule our minds and bodies. In perhaps the most revealing sentence in *The Second Machine Age*, the authors report that they have "never seen a truly creative machine, or an entrepreneurial one, or an innovative one."[22] Here lies the book's message of class hierarchy in its most transparent form. Since Brynjolfsson and McAfee are confident that neither *their* jobs nor *their* social power will worsen, their advocacy for limited redistribution is ultimately the magnanimity of enlightened bosses, the moralism of the "winners" who prefer to paternalistically manage the "losers" rather than challenge the economic and political hierarchies that create such a distinction in the first place.

"Technology is not destiny. We shape our destiny." If Brynjolfsson and McAfee's final lines in *The Second Machine Age* sound like a refreshing departure from technological determinism, it is only because the agency in question is their own.

Notes

1 "50/ Erik Brynjolfsson & Andrew McAfee," The Politico 50, *Politico Magazine*, www.politico.com/magazine/politico50/2014/erik-brynjolfsson-50.html.

2 "Artificial Intelligence, Automation, and the Economy" uses Brynjolfsson and McAfee's concept of automation "superstars" and even perhaps cribs their book's final line about technology and destiny (see the end of this chapter). The 2013 panel's agenda, transcripts, and PowerPoint presentations can be found in the Obama White House online archive: https://obamawhitehouse.archives.gov/adm inistration/eop/ostp/pcast/meetings/past.

3 Brynjolfsson and McAfee, *The Second Machine Age*, 9–11.

4 Barack Obama, interview with Joi Ito and Scott Dadich, *Wired*, November 2016, www.wired.com/2016/10/president-obama-mit-joi-ito-interview/. On the ideologies of *Wired*, see Eran Fisher, *Media and New Capitalism in the Digital Age: The Spirit of Networks* (New York: Palgrave, 2010).

5 Steve Lohroct, "More Jobs Predicted for Machines, Not People," *The New York Times*, October 23, 2011, www.nytimes.com/2011/10/24/technology/economists -see-more-jobs-for-machines-not-people.html?scp=1&sq=brynjolfsson&st=cse.

6 Quoted in Lohroct.

7 Erik Brynjolfsson, and Andrew McAfee, *Race against the Machine: How the Digital Revolution is Accelerating Innovation, Driving Productivity, and Irreversibly Transforming Employment and the Economy* (Lexington, MA: Digital Frontier Press), chap. 1, Kindle.

8 Brynjolfsson and McAfee, *Second Machine Age*, 133.

9 Brynjolfsson and McAfee, 231.

10 Brynjolfsson and McAfee, 41.

11 Cyrus C. M. Mody, *The Long Arm of Moore's Law: Microelectronics and American Science* (Cambridge, MA: MIT Press, 2017), 5, my emphasis.

12 Mody, 9.

13 Brynjolfsson and McAfee, *Second Machine Age*, 42.

14 Frank Pasquale, "To Replace or Respect: Futurology as if People Mattered," *b2o*, January 20, 2015, www.boundary2.org/2015/01/to-replace-or-respect-futurology -as-if-people-mattered/.

15 Andrew McAfee, "Defending the Free Market in Davos," MIT Initiative on the Digital Economy (blog), February 3, 2016, http://ide.mit.edu/news-blog/blog/d efending-free-market-davos.

16 Brynjolfsson and McAfee, *Second Machine Age*, 245.

17 Mariana Mazzucato, *The Value of Everything: Making and Taking in the Global Economy* (London: Allen Lane, 2018). Brynjolfsson and McAfee cite Mazzucato's earlier book, *The Entrepreneurial State: Debunking Public vs. Private Sector Myths* (New York: Anthem Press, 2013) and acknowledge that the government has funded many of the second machine age's technologies. Their entrepreneurial rhetoric is thus a classic case of disavowal: they know that innovators rely on the public to socialize research and development, but they act as if they don't know.

18 Brynjolfsson and McAfee, *Second Machine Age*, 214.

19 Broussard defines *technochauvism* as the "belief that tech is always the solution." It is usually accompanied by "Ayn Randian meritocracy," "technolibertarian political values," belief that "computers are more 'objective' or 'unbiased'

because they distill questions and answers down to mathematical evaluation," and "unwavering faith that if the world just used more computers, and used them properly, social problems would disappear." Broussard, *Artificial Unintelligence*, 7–8.
20 Brynjolfsson and McAfee, *Second Machine Age*, 148.
21 Brynjolfsson and McAfee, 231.
22 Brynjolfsson and McAfee, 191.

3   The Terminator, or The Automation Fetish

If Moore's Law is business sf's ur-myth, the Terminator is the sf that the genre finds most exasperating. The Terminator is the Hitler of automation mythologies. In a 1994 *Wired* article, Mike Godwin coined Godwin's Law of Nazi Analogies: "As an online discussion grows longer, the probability of a comparison involving Nazis or Hitler approaches one."[1] I would like to propose Ramirez's Law of Terminator Analogies: as a discussion of automation grows longer, the probability of a comparison involving the *Terminator* franchise approaches one.

Scientists, engineers, and business sf writers complain that the Terminator has warped the public's imagination. Seventy-two percent of Americans report feeling "somewhat" or "very" worried about automation.[2] But when people realize that the technology is less advanced than they imagined, they feel underwhelmed. While John Jordan, professor at Penn State University's Smeal College of Business, acknowledges that genre sf's "rich mythologies" frame how we imagine automation, he treats genre sf as a distraction from actual robotics and the real ethical and economic questions it raises.[3] With one hand, business sf compares the latest technologies to genre sf in order to impress us with the claim that entrepreneurs have realized the old dreams; with the other, business sf waves away analogies to genre sf so that we can temper our hopes and appreciate the small steps of capitalist progress. Once business sf writers and other experts have schooled the public in the proper modesty, the Terminator analogy should disappear.

The Terminator is indeed far removed from the state of the art in automation, but there is truth in the embellishment: the truth of domination. Under capitalism, domination—the rule of arbitrary power—takes a particular form: deliberate action is subject to the aggregate and opaque choices of myriad market actors. A boss may decide that it is ethical to pay employees higher wages, a worker may reason that a particular job is not satisfying, or a consumer might support a local shop against its corporate rival, but their choices are overruled by the cumulative and incontestable effects of myriad actors' producing, buying, selling, and laboring. The boss risks greater competition from businesses that pay workers less; the worker feels compelled to take the job before a more desperate worker does; the local shop closes down because it cannot compete with its rival's low prices. The boss, worker, and consumer are social agents insofar as they are interacting with other people, but they do not deliberate with these others and will never meet most of them. For Marx, market forces are ultimately social relations among people, but since this sociality is forged through the market's abstract mediation— the "invisible hand"—it moves behind our backs and takes on a fetishized form, "the fantastic form of a relation between things." More than a mere illusion, this fetishism is rooted in the lived abstractions of market interdependence and, more broadly, the "bewitched, distorted and upside-down world" of capitalism.[4]

When technology is market-dependent, collective decisions about technology tend to be reduced to the consumption of goods and services that elites have designed. To the extent that technology becomes a bearer of the market's domination, the more it, too, assumes the fetishized form of a "movement of things." *The Terminator is this movement of technological things*—the speculative refraction of a social organization of technology that, because it happens behind our backs, appears to be not only autonomous but malevolent. The first film in the Terminator franchise appeared during a massive restructuring of the US automobile industry that resulted in plant closures and thousands of layoffs. While declining sales and competition from Japan were widely recognized as the roots of the crisis, some analysts suggested that robotization was the true cause and would trigger millions of auto layoffs in the near future.[5] *The Terminator* (1984) condenses and inverts this economic fiction in the sequence in which the cyborg traps Sarah and Reese in, appropriately, an automated factory. Whereas in Marx's account the social relations among people adopt the fantastic form of relations among things, the cyborg's humanoid skin has been burned away to reveal a metal skeleton. What appeared to be human *really is* an autonomous thing. And like the market itself, the cyborg, Reese explains, "can't be bargained with. It can't be reasoned with. It doesn't feel pity, or remorse, or fear." In the figure of the Terminator sf literalizes and "thingifies" the abstractness of capitalist technosocial relations; it offers a special kind of mimesis of vast interdependencies—the totality of market actions that shape technology—in which we are enmeshed but cannot effectively contest.[6] When Sarah uses a hydraulic press to crush the cyborg, *The Terminator* offers a symbolic solution to the problem: if ordinary people can control automation, we can repurpose the automated factory to defeat autonomous technology.[7]

Business sf has a different solution. The slippage in *The Second Machine Age* between technological determinism and innovation is a form of appearance of the contradiction between market domination and narratives of individual responsibility and meritocracy. The inventors of market freedom argued that even if our lives are determined by uncontrollable market forces, this situation is not coercive if no identifiable individual or group intends to coerce us. The market's indirect domination is preferable to exactly this alternative: *direct* domination by other people.[8] But how can we square subjection to the aggregate choices of market actors with the claim that capitalist society is not only free, but is the only system that truly incentivizes and rewards individual effort and talent? Friedrich Hayek's answer was that meritocracy, like Moore's Law, is an economic fiction that is made true when people act *as if* it were true: "Though a man's conviction that all he achieves is due solely to his exertions, skill, and intelligence may be largely false [...] the belief that success depends wholly on him is probably the pragmatically most effective incentive to successful action."[9] This solution is not good enough for Brynjolfsson and McAfee, however. The authors' story that entrepreneurs should manage the second machine age is an attempt to put a benign human face on impersonal processes that they want to keep beyond the reach of popular political contestation. Although engineers, scientists, and capitalists are also subject to the whims of the market, the top 1% have nonetheless benefited immensely from the "objective" movement of digital technology in free markets. Their automation myths are hegemonic narratives that seek to win consent for their leadership of automated capitalism. Yet the narratives can be convincing only if they transform the market's caprice into the just rewards of individual "brilliance"—if they can suppress the Terminator as the figure of capital's abstract domination. More precisely, their preferred Terminator is the cyborg of *Terminator 2* (1991), a reprogrammed and domesticated machine that serves as the ultimate tool of accumulation and thus embodies "the massive hubris of the capitalist class that believes it can control the forces it has unleashed."[10]

Audiences at the original screenings of *The Terminator* were said to have cheered whenever the machine brutally dispatched punks, housewives, police, or anyone else who had the misfortune of crossing it. The nuclear historian Paul Brians surmised that the audience was "cheering for its own annihilation." Similarly, when Arnold Schwarzenegger was elected governor of California, the sf critic Carl Freedman interpreted his victory as a symptom of Californians' cynical, reactionary identification with the Terminator's anti-human power.[11] While I think these interpretations are correct, the Terminator might also be useful for technoclastic thinking because it is a disavowed symptom of automation myths. The Terminator is not a distortion to be dispelled by experts—a mere abstract negation of abstract social relations. The killer cyborg is the speculative truth of a false world in which our capacity to flourish with and through technology has only the most tenuous links to popular decision-making. The Terminator will not disappear until popular deliberation, free from arbitrary power, shapes technological change. Thus, the determinate negation of business sf and the automation fetish is democratic technology.

I will return to the question of alternatives in my conclusion. Instead of proceeding straightway to the future, we should de-automate business sf's extrapolative method and turn instead to the past. For the study of business sf's historical myths further elucidates what its futures take for granted. Karen and Barbara Fields have suggested the following modification of Santayana's famous maxim: "those who do not learn from history will have no idea what they are repeating."[12] In the case of automation myths, this can be translated as: those who cannot remember the past won't know what histories they have set to automatically repeat.

Notes

1   Mike Godwin, "Meme, Counter-Meme," *Wired*, October 1, 1994, www.wired .com/1994/10/godwin-if-2/.
2   Pew Research Center, "Automation in Everyday Life," 3.
3   John Jordan, *Robots*, The MIT Press Essential Knowledge Series (Cambridge, MA: MIT Press, 2016), 67. See also Harry Collins, *Artifictional Intelligence: Against Humanity's Surrender to Computers* (Cambridge, UK: Polity, 2018).
4   Marx, *Capital*, 164–5; Karl Marx, *Capital: A Critique of Political Economy*, vol. 3, trans. David Fernbach (Harmondsworth, UK: Penguin Classics, 1991), 969. This account of domination is indebted to William Clare Roberts.
5   Robert F. Arnold, "Termination or Transformation? The 'Terminator' Films and Recent Changes in the U. S. Auto Industry," *Film Quarterly* 52, no. 1 (1998): 20–30.
6   This formulation of sf's aesthetics draws on Carl Freedman's reading of Philip K. Dick's literalization of commodity fetishism and Seo-Young Chu's theory of sf mimesis. See Carl Freedman, "Towards a Theory of Paranoia: The Science Fiction of Philip K. Dick," *Science Fiction Studies* 11, no. 1 (1984): 15–24, and Seo-Young Chu, *Do Metaphors Dream of Literal Sleep? A Science-Fictional Theory of Representation* (Cambridge, MA: Harvard University Press, 2010).
7   Arnold, "Termination or Transformation?" 25.
8   Eric MacGilvray, *The Invention of Market Freedom* (Cambridge: Cambridge University Press, 2011), 171–2.
9   F. A. Hayek, *The Collected Works of F. A. Hayek*, vol. 17, *The Constitution of Liberty*, ed. Ronald Hamowy (New York: Routledge, 2011), 145.
10 Dyer-Witheford, Kjøsen, and Steinhoff, *Inhuman Power*, 4.
11 Paul Brians, "Terminator vs. Terminator: Nuclear Holocaust as a Video Game," Washington State University, https://brians.wsu.edu/2016/12/02/terminator-vs -terminator/. Carl Freedman, "Polemical Afterword: Some Brief Reflections on Arnold Schwarzenegger and on Science Fiction in Contemporary American Culture," *PMLA* 119, no. 3 (2004): 539–46.
12 Karen E. Fields, and Barbara J. Fields, *Racecraft: The Soul of Inequality in American Life* (London: Verso, 2012), 63.

Part II
Original Automation

4   When Farmers Lost
Their "Jobs"

When business sf divines the future of work, it not only extrapolates current trends but also writes alternate histories. To take one of myriad examples, Jerry Kaplan claims that "as recently as the early 1800s, farms employed a remarkable 80 percent of U.S. workers. [...] But by 1900, that figure had dropped in half, to 40 percent, and today it's only 1.5 percent, including unpaid family and undocumented workers." Kaplan concludes: "Basically, we managed to automate nearly everyone out of a job, but instead of causing widespread unemployment, we freed people up for a host of other productive and wealth-producing activities."[1] Kaplan's narrative is reminiscent of Cold War modernization theory, a capitalist Hegelianism in which labor-saving technology acts as the World Spirit and lifts history up through ever higher stages of freedom and wealth: agriculture, manufacturing, services.[2] In each stage, automation lays jobs on the slaughter-bench of history but also creates new and better ones. Automation worked out in the past, so it will work out in the future. Now that robots and AI are eliminating the last manufacturing jobs and taking over services, we can expect technology to generate new jobs even if we can't currently imagine them. Although Ford's prediction of a jobless future starkly contrasts with Kaplan's optimism, business dystopians differ from utopians like Kaplan only insofar as their World Spirit has grown so powerful that it threatens *all* jobs; the dystopians interpret the utopians' inability to name the jobs of the future as a revelation of the limits of human labor as such.

The story of farmers who lost their "jobs" and were "freed" for manufacturing is a mythical origin story of American automation. Drawing on Marx's account of "primitive" or original (*ursprünglich*) accumulation, I call this story the "original accumulation of automation," or "original automation" for short. Marx recognized that classical political economy's explanations of the origins of capitalism were mytho-poetry. The primitive accumulation of capital "plays approximately the same role in political economy as original sin does in theology." The story, in short, goes as follows: the "diligent, intelligent and above all frugal elite" saved and accumulated, while the "lazy rascals" spent everything until they had nothing left but their capacity to labor for the elite. In contrast, Marx's counternarrative of the violent dispossession of the peasantry emphasizes that "capital comes dripping from head to toe, from every pore, with blood and dirt."[3]

Similarly, the myth of original automation is a sanitized history that washes the "blood and dirt" from American capitalism. To explain how automation will develop in the future, business sf constructs a counterfactual history in which the antebellum United States was already capitalist, farmers already had "jobs" to lose to technology, and factories later swelled with displaced agricultural workers seeking new and better "opportunities." Where the automation mythologist sees labor floating from one capitalist job to another within the smooth, timeless, abstract space of "development," the student of capitalist history sees the material terrain of dispossession and struggles around settler colonialism, race, gender, and class.

Although American capitalism developed unevenly in time and space and took myriad hybrid forms before its consolidation after the Civil War, we can avoid missing capitalism's forest for its trees with the help of the concept of market dependence. Marx's account of primitive accumulation spotlights propertyless proletarians who are free in a double sense: legally free to possess and contract their own bodies and labor power, and free from their own means of production and subsistence. The latter is the former's material basis. For dispossessed workers who cannot produce and reproduce their own lives, the labor market does not function as a mere *opportunity* to sell labor power but rather as a *necessity* to earn wages in order to eat. Although markets are ancient, only in capitalism do markets acquire a generalized power of compulsion. Capitalist owners of means of production are also subject to the market imperative to produce competitively and profitably, which necessitates constant transformation and cheapening of the production process. In other words, while workers depend on markets to reproduce themselves, employers depend on markets to remain employers. A capitalist who cannot compete with other capitalists will soon become an ex-capitalist. Thus, a society can be called capitalist if its social property relations and corresponding strategies of social production and reproduction systematically force actors to compete and succeed in the market.[4]

It is misleading to claim that around 1800 "farms employed a remarkable 80 percent of U.S. workers" because the terms "employed" and "workers" imply that the great majority of antebellum farmers were fully dependent on the market as wage laborers. Kaplan makes the implication explicit when he anachronistically claims that farmers were automated out of their "jobs," a term that most farmers at the time would have associated not with regular wage labor, the term's dominant meaning today, but with occasional work ("jobbing") and cheating ("jobbery").[5] Many northern farmers hired seasonal farm hands and took on boarders, but permanent agricultural wage labor was not a dominant social form. Wage labor in the north and south approached 50% of total social labor only after the Civil War.[6] Most antebellum northern farmers owned their farms, and farm labor was largely supplied by unpaid family members.[7] Antebellum farmers avoided wage labor because they understood it in terms that would have been familiar to the ancient Greeks and Romans: it was a state of dependency only a hair's breadth removed from indenture and slavery (to which I will return in the following chapter). Not that these debased forms of labor were wrong per se, only wrong for white settlers and European co-ethnics. As Aziz Rana has shown, the settler-republican ideology of free labor was non-universal and required expropriation of native land and subordination of the labor of slaves, domestic servants, and women and children. Some could be free only because others were not.

Yet if around 1800 the vast majority of farmers were neither wage laborers nor employed large numbers of wage laborers, the northern family farm was rapidly becoming market-dependent. While most did not have to sell their capacity to labor, farmers in New England and the west increasingly faced pressure to specialize, produce more cheaply, and sell at a profit. Just as a factory owner is subject to the market imperative to produce competitively and faces the loss of his factory if he does not do so, the northern farmer's social reproduction tied unsuccessful commercial agriculture to the loss of the farmer's primary means of production and subsistence, his land and farm. The historical stage thus seems to be set for original automation: have we not arrived at technology's "disruption" of traditional agriculture, the substitution of mechanical power, steam, electricity, and petroleum for animal and human muscle, a great leap forward in agricultural efficiency, and the "freeing" of farmers for the next stage of historical evolution? To be sure, the early decades of the nineteenth century witnessed a dramatic growth in agricultural productivity thanks to mechanization, new seeds and fertilizers, and crop rotation methods. There was a switch from what environmental historian J. R. McNeill terms the "somatic energy regime," fueled by the body's conversion and use of biomass, to the "exosomatic energy regime," fueled by coal and oil. At the start of the century, a crop of wheat demanded 56 hours of labor, and each farmer produced enough food to feed about four people; by century's end, wheat required only about fifteen labor hours and a typical farmer produced enough for seven people.[8] If we ignore the important fact that immigration from Ireland and Germany in the 1840s and from southern and eastern Europe toward century's end created the first reserve army of wage labor in the United States, it might sound plausible that labor-saving technology reduced demand for agricultural labor and created a labor pool for the emerging factory system.

But why did farmers systematically invest in new productive technologies? Business sf's answer is that this is simply what "rational business owners" do. By assuming that capitalist rationality is pre-given as human nature, this answer will always beg the question: why did antebellum northern farmers whose means of production and subsistence were relatively independent from the market start acting like rational capitalists? From roughly the colonial period to the Jacksonian era, northern farmers were embedded in what James Parisot calls the "patriarchal household mode of social reproduction." Husbands and male elders organized household farm labor around subsistence and sold surpluses on the market. Although men occupied the dominant positions in the gender hierarchy, the household was not yet reified as the domain of women, a moral space of non-work that serves as a haven from the cut-throat world of men and competitive markets. For example, cooking was women's work, but husbands participated by gathering, cutting, and stacking wood for fireplaces that they had built themselves, by milling the corn or wheat grain that thickened their wives' stews, and by whittling the spoons that wives used to stir them. Wives, in turn, helped husbands in the fields. The goal of production was not accumulation but economic independence and land to bequeath to male heirs. While farmers were never completely self-sufficient, the market had not yet remade social relations in its own image:

> they spoke in a language of "give and take" rather than "buy and sell" and exchange relations were built into community and kinship relations. Neighbors swapped labor, depending on resources and community obligation. And debts were exchanged in services and labor, although occasionally money, and were built on social trust as they often went for many years without being settled.[9]

The patriarchal household mode of social reproduction was materially contingent on a web of social property relations that encompassed cheap land, conquest of native territories, low taxes, and successful class struggles against land speculators, debt collectors, and merchants. When land speculation inflated the price of land, railroad companies took the best land in the west, and states raised taxes to pay for war debts, the patriarchal household mode of social reproduction broke down. Farmers had no choice but to implement technologies that maximized their market success and generated cash for mortgage payments, taxes, and land for their sons. Charles Post explains that

> only rural producers whose continued possession of land and other means of production require successful commodity-production are subject to the "law of value" and must specialise output, systematically reinvest

surpluses and develop the productivity of land and labour through technical innovation.[10]

Farmers who failed to rationalize production did not lose their jobs; they
lost their *farms*. Alongside immigrants, some dispossessed northern farmers
became industrial wage laborers.

Yet even here American history defies business sf's reified stages of
growth. There was never a general shift of social labor from agriculture to
manufacturing. Although the amount of social labor in agriculture declined
precipitously in the nineteenth century while industrial labor swelled, it was
service labor that surpassed agricultural labor around 1870. In fact, service
labor has been larger than industrial labor for most of US history.[11]

Thus, we must radically rewrite the basic narrative structure of original
automation. In the north, agricultural automation was a means of negotiat-
ing a crisis in the social property and re/productive relations of settlerism.
The true actants in this drama are dispossessed white settlers, not liberated
farmers; land speculators and debt collectors, not genius inventors who gave
new technologies to eager rural entrepreneurs; market necessity, not market opportunity. While business sf imagines neatly interconnected chapters
in the past, present, and future of capitalism and technology, the technoclastic thinker must follow Walter Benjamin's advice and "blast a specific
era out of the homogeneous course of history."[12] For only by understanding
the past's specificity can we see the "blood and dirt" of settler colonialism,
race, patriarchy, and class struggles in the transformation of the non- and
proto-capitalist elements of the antebellum north into capitalist agriculture.
Once we situate automation in its concrete history, we can identify the true
continuities.

Notes

1 Kaplan, *Humans Need Not Apply*, 133. See also Ford, *Rise of the Robots*, ix, 23.
2 On business sf's Hegelianism, see George Caffentzis, *Letters of Blood and
   Fire: Work, Machines, and the Crisis of Capitalism* (Oakland, CA: PM Press,
   2013), 70.
3 Marx, *Capital*, vol. 1, 873, 926.
4 On capitalism's uneven development in the United States, see James Parisot,
   *How America Became Capitalist: Imperial Expansion and the Conquest of the
   West* (London: Pluto, 2019) and Charles Post, *The American Road to Capitalism:
   Studies in Class-Structure, Economic Development and Political Conflict, 1620–
   1877* (Leiden, the Netherlands: Brill, 2011). On the market as opportunity and
   imperative, see Ellen Meiksins Wood, *The Origin of Capitalism: A Longer View*
   (New York: Verso, 2017). On social property relations and rules of reproduction,
   see Robert Brenner, "Property and Progress: Where Adam Smith Went Wrong,"
   in *Marxist History-Writing for the Twenty-First Century*, ed. Chris Wickham
   (Oxford, UK: Oxford University Press, 2007), 49–111.

5 Raymond Williams, *Keywords: A Vocabulary of Culture and Society* (New York: Oxford University Press, 2015), 267.

6 Parisot, *How America Became Capitalist*, 162.

7 Post, *The American Road*, 41, 96.

8 J. R. McNeill, *Something New Under the Sun: An Environmental History of the Twentieth-Century World* (New York: Norton, 2000), chap. 1; Carroll W. Pursell, *The Machine in America: A Social History of Technology* (Baltimore, MD: Johns Hopkins University Press, 2007), 119; Post, *The American Road*, 93–4.

9 Parisot, *How America Became Capitalist*, 55–6. Compare to Post, *The American Road*, 47–8. Historians of US capitalism must carefully navigate between the devil of naturalizing and eternalizing capitalism and the deep blue sea of reinforcing the ideology of the self-sufficient yeoman farmer. Though she comes perilously close at times to suggesting that the colonies were thoroughly market dependent and thus capitalist from the start, Ruth Schwartz Cowan debunks the myth of self-sufficiency in *A Social History of American Technology* (New York: Oxford University Press, 1997), chap. 2. On the historical co-constitution of female domesticity and male market individualism, see Stephanie Coontz, *The Way We Never Were: American Families and the Nostalgia Trap* (New York: Basic Books, 1992), chap. 3. On the division of labor in the colonial household, see Cowan, *More Work for Mother*, chap. 2.

10 Post, *The American Road*, 57.

11 Louis D. Johnston, "History Lessons: Understanding the Decline in Manufacturing," *MinnPost*, February 22, 2012, www.minnpost.com/macro-micro-minnesota/2012/02/history-lessons-understanding-decline-manufacturing/.

12 Walter Benjamin, "On the Concept of History," in *Selected Writings, vol. 4, 1938–1940*, eds. Howard Eiland and Michael W. Jennings, trans. Harry Zohn (Cambridge, MA: Harvard University Press, 2003), 396.

5   Techno-republicanism

Slave plantations are a conspicuous omission in the myth of original automation. This silence serves the opposite function of the myth's anachronistic description of farmers who lost their "jobs." If the latter posits full-blown capitalist wage labor in the antebellum past, the exclusion of plantation owners from the class of "farmers" conceals the capitalist nature of American slavery. Plantations were thoroughly market dependent. Owners had to sell at a profit in order to pay taxes, wages to overseers, and debts that they incurred when they bought their land and slaves. Owners who failed to compete on the market faced foreclosure on their means of production. The historical sociologist John J. Clegg estimates that over half of all slaves sold in South Carolina in the 1840s had gone to market after being confiscated from their previous owners by creditors.[1] Instead of being an archaic system that was replaced by free labor and rational markets, slavery has accounted for plenty of the blood and dirt in capitalism's history.

Slavery's social property relations and logics of production and reproduction made rationalization of productivity an imperative. Especially after the 1807 Act Prohibiting Importation of Slaves, automation played an important role in raising the productivity of the domestic slave labor force—a role that business sf cannot but disavow. Although he exaggerates its system-wide effects, the historian Edward E. Baptist is correct to identify the overseer's whip as a productivity tool. For the whip was a brutal capitalist instrument of labor discipline with which the overseer automated enslaved people's hands and reduced them to self-acting cotton-picking machines. One planter remarked that the hands of whipped slaves moved as if "some new motive power was applied in the process."[2] This new motive power was the human body's internal automation, a set of muscle reflexes that slaves learned through the whip's evil pedagogy. The philosopher Bernard Stiegler has suggested that technology is exteriorization, "the pursuit of life by means other than life."[3] The whip was the exteriorization of the slaver's will, the pursuit of white life by means of automated black life, the pure form of what the black revolutionary union movements of the late 1960s dubbed "niggermation."[4]

Whitney's cotton gin was even more consequential for productivity growth. The gin complemented the whip: after slaves were terrorized into picking cotton as quickly and mechanically as possible, the gin "exteriorized" the further technical action of their hands because they could only slowly separate seeds from cotton fibers. Whitney's gin displaced the technical action of the slave's fingers, which were now used to turn the machine's crank and set its mechanism in motion. Combined with territorial conquest and expansion, and solidified by the planters' political power, the gin's automation of seed extraction contributed to a massive growth of enslaved cotton production in the south: "In 1790, three years before Whitney's invention, the United States had produced 1.5 million pounds of cotton; in 1800 that number grew to 36.5 million pounds, and in 1820 to 167.5 million pounds."[5]

What if slavery's automation not only paralleled the emergence of capitalist agriculture and manufacturing in the north, but was the more radically capitalist project? In other words, technoclastic critique should turn the myth of original automation on its head, so that slavery, this allegedly "primitive" stage of history, is an ideal toward which fully developed capitalist automation still tends. I am intrigued by Clegg's claims that slavery is "pristinely capitalist" and that "in a capitalist order of fully specified property rights, it is wage labor rather than slave labor that is the anomaly."[6] Not only is the slave's labor a commodity bought and sold on the market, the slave *is* a commodity with no legal ownership of their body. If the totally commodified and subjected worker is capitalism's model labor power, then automation can be understood not as the movement of freedom and the World Spirit through history but rather as the perfection of servitude by technical means.

Consider a 1926 General Electric advertisement titled "Slaves," which depicts a dark-skinned man carrying a large log on his shoulders. His loincloth and headwear suggest that he is from the ancient past, perhaps Egypt. Beside the man is a quotation from Oscar Wilde: "civilization requires slaves. The Greeks were quite right there. [...] Human slavery is wrong, insecure, and demoralizing. On mechanical slavery, on the slavery of the machine, the future of the world depends." Below the image and the quote, the main copy presents GE electric motors as "America's slaves": "Through their service American workers do more, earn more, and produce quality goods at lower cost than anywhere else in the world."[7] If GE used the image of ancient slavery to sidestep America's *actual* slaves, a novelty robot built by Westinghouse Electric Corporation was less circumspect. Created in 1930, Rastus the Mechanical Negro had dark skin and wooly hair and was dressed in a sharecropper's overalls and neckerchief. The dream of substituting technology for black bodies has rarely been represented with such shameless sincerity.[8]

Desires for new labor-saving technology and for a technologically perfected slavery are tightly intertwined in automation myths. In one of the myth's oldest iterations, Aristotle connected Homer's description of the gods' technology to slavery:

> if every tool could perform its own work when ordered, or by seeing what to do in advance, like the statues of Daedalus in the story, or the tripods of Hephaestus which the poet says "enter self-moved [*autómatos*] the company divine," if thus shuttles wove and quills played harps of themselves [*autai*], master-craftsmen would have no need of assistants [*hupērétēs*; underlings] and masters no need of slaves.[9]

The passage presupposes the ancient Athenian view that citizens require leisure, and thus freedom from labor, to develop the virtues of self-governance. When Wilde claims in the quote in the GE ad that "civilization requires slaves," he echoes the Athenian understanding of the good life as entailing the citizen's economic independence, which is made possible by the citizen's command over slave labor and lordship over women and children in the household. Athenian men could be free political actors in public space because they were masters and despots in private domestic space.[10] Yet in the passage from *Politics* cited above, Aristotle speculates that if technical instruments could follow commands or were otherwise *autómatos*, self-willed and unbidden, they would perform the exact political-economic function of slaves and servants and thus make the latter unnecessary. Note, however, that Aristotle's automation is not a *critique* of subjection. It simply provides slavery by other means. The concept of freedom as independence achieved on the backs of slaves, servants, and domestic labor remains firmly in place.

General Electric's ad and Westinghouse's robot are prime examples of what I call American "techno-republicanism."[11] Techno-republicanism shares modern republicanism's definition of freedom as non-domination but repudiates the classical republican argument that slavery is necessary for the citizen's freedom. To be more precise: *human* slavery. The techno-republican doesn't want to abolish slavery but technologize it. Describing his co-author Brynjolfsson's concept of "digital Athens," McAfee endorses Aristotle's concept of leisure while rejecting human slavery:

> The Athenian citizens had lives of leisure; they got to participate in democracy and create art. That was largely because they had slaves to do the work. Okay, I don't want human slaves, but in a very, very automated

and digitally productive economy you don't need to work as much, as hard, with as many people, to get the fruits of the economy.

Everything hinges on McAfee's "but." No, he does not want human slaves; nonetheless, slavery can be redeemed. Human slavery is obviously wrong, yet a different kind of slavery will free us from "toil and drudgery."[12]

What enables the contrary thought is technology. Techno-republicanism uses automation to solve a contradiction that arises when universality is added to republicanism: "The particularism of a commitment to republican liberty—independence for a particular class, dependence for another class—logically conflicts with the universalism of the commitment to human equality."[13] In other words, if republicans believe that the self-rule of the few necessitates the domination of the many, how can they square this belief with the principle that all humans are equal, hence equally worthy of freedom? The techno-republican solution is slavery without human slaves, and thus without racism, colonialism, or patriarchy. Substituting for dominated labor, automation eliminates the dependent class and universalizes independence. But in dreaming up a technical fix for slavery, techno-republicans retain the relationality of freedom and subjection. Digital Athens is still Athens, and freedom remains freedom from labor that has been "exteriorized" and outsourced to an actor that can be controlled despotically. Thus, techno-republicanism's universality is *the universality of the master*. Automation redeems America's slave past by enabling everyone to enjoy the leisure that the slaver extracted from the slave.

One of the most remarkable representations of techno-republican desire in recent genre sf is the HBO series *Westworld* (2016–). The series is an sf western that takes place in a theme park that recreates the mythical space of the American frontier, complete with ranches, saloons, brothels, Union and Confederate soldiers, shoot-outs with Mexican bandits, and skirmishes with "blood-thirsty savages." The park is staffed by androids who are nearly indistinguishable from human guests and whose "job" it is to entertain them. While some guests participate in complex immersive narratives alongside the androids, others use the androids to indulge simpler desires for wanton violence and rape. The androids cannot harm the guests and are condemned to repeat their programmed scripts, which can include their violent death. Their memories are deleted at the end of a sequence.

What might initially seem like an odd mashup of sf and the western perfectly combines automation myths and settlerism into a capitalist techno-republican utopia. The androids are not only a totally commodified and controllable slave labor force; they are even better than human slaves because they do exactly what they are told, laboring automatically in algorithmically generated ideological narratives, and can be restored after being beaten or killed. They embody and substitute for the colonized, racialized, and gendered others that actual settlers expropriated, enslaved, and excluded from the sphere of freedom. Rana's two faces of American freedom thus map rather directly onto the faces of guests and androids: the first group exists in a restricted sphere of freedom and equality, while the second group's unfree labor and exclusion are the material basis of the first group's liberty. The androids' absolute subjection positions guests as slave masters and despots, liberating them from "toil and drudgery" and opening up the properly human space of play and enjoyment. Although class privilege remains—the park is expensive and the guests are wealthy—the position of the master has been "democratized" and made formally "accessible" to all paying customers, regardless of race, gender, or sexuality. When the androids begin to recall their traumatic memories, it is nothing less than American history, the bad conscience of capitalist techno-republicanism, that weighs like a nightmare on the brains of the artificially living.

Techno-republicans have yet to build Westworld. The series is not a prediction but a distillation of the ways in which history shapes the automation imaginary. As Part III will demonstrate, dreams of domination continue to inform fictions of the technosocial future. These dreams stand before us like ghosts of futures past, warning us that to accelerate automation is to risk automating the power fantasies that pervade American history. Where automation cannot completely replace the dominated, it invisibilizes and controls laboring bodies more efficiently. In other cases, we will see that the "rise of the robots" thesis is too caught up by the World Spirt of capitalist progress to reckon with the system's crises.

Notes

1 John J. Clegg, "Capitalism and Slavery," *Critical Historical Studies* 2, no. 2 (2015): 300.
2 Edward E. Baptist, *The Half Has Never Been Told: Slavery and the Making of American Capitalism* (New York: Basic Books, 2016), Kindle edition, chap. 4. For a critique of Baptist's argument that whipping can explain system-wide productivity gains on cotton plantations, see Clegg, "Capitalism and Slavery," 289–95.
3 Bernard Stiegler, *Technics and Time,* vol. 1, *The Fault of Epimetheus*, trans. Richard Beardsworth and George Collins (Stanford, CA: Stanford University Press, 1998), 17.
4 Dan Georgakas, and Marvin Surkin, *Detroit: I Do Mind Dying: A Study in Urban Revolution*, rev. ed. (Cambridge, MA: South End Press, 1999).
5 Sven Beckert, *Empire of Cotton: A Global History* (New York: Vintage, 2015), 106.
6 Clegg, "Capitalism and Slavery," 302–3.

7 Tobias Higbie, "Why Do Robots Rebel? The Labor History of a Cultural Icon," *Labor: Studies in Working-Class History of the Americas* 10, no. 1 (2013): 115–6. While Higbie found the ad in a 1926 issue of *Journal of Electrical Workers and Operators,* it seems to have appeared in a range of popular magazines and newspapers. The *General Electric News* claimed that it "will appear in the Saturday Evening Post, December 25, and in December issues of several other general magazines." "Slaves," *General Electric News, Fort Wayne Works* 10, no. 12 (December 1926): 24.

8 For a genealogy of the mechanical slave, see Bob Johnson, *Mineral Rites: An Archaeology of the Fossil Economy* (Baltimore, MD: Johns Hopkins University Press, 2019), chap. 3.

9 Aristotle, *Politics* 1.1253b. The original text, translations, and a wealth of reference materials are available at the Perseus Digital Library: www.perseus.tufts.edu/hopper/collection?collection=Perseus:collection:Greco-Roman.

10 Hannah Arendt, *The Human Condition* (Chicago, IL: University of Chicago Press, 1958), chap. 5.

11 I am riffing here on Atanasoski and Vora's concept of "technoliberalism."

12 Andrew McAfee, interview with Antonio Regalado, "When Machines Do Your Job," *MIT Technology Review*, July 11, 2012, www.technologyreview.com/s/428429/when-machines-do-your-job/. See also Max Tegmark, *Life 3.0: Being Human in the Age of Artificial Intelligence* (New York: Knopf, 2017), chap. 3.

13 Alex Gourevitch, *From Slavery to the Cooperative Commonwealth: Labor and Republican Liberty in the Nineteenth Century* (New York: Cambridge University Press, 2015), 19.

Part III
Disenchanted Objects

6   The Misadventures of Baxter and Sawyer

There seems to be a plainly obvious explanation behind increasing automation. In *Rise of the Robots*, Martin Ford echoes much of Brynjolfsson and McAfee's account but suggests that their advocacy for labor-augmenting automation is naïve:

> The bottom line is that, despite all the rhetoric about "job creators," rational business owners do *not want* to hire more workers: they hire people only because they have to. The progression toward ever more automation is not an artifact of "design philosophy" or the personal preferences of engineers: it is fundamentally driven by capitalism. […] For any rational business, the adoption of labor-saving technology will almost invariably prove to be irresistible. Changing that would require far more than an appeal to engineers and designers: it would require modifying the basic incentives built into the market economy.[1]

Ford shares Brynjolfsson and McAfee's reluctance to transcend capitalism or "the basic incentives built into the market economy." But while they prop up the system's virtues by emphasizing capitalists' and engineers' talent and creativity, Ford argues that market rationality will cause widespread technological displacement that only a universal basic income can mitigate. His business sf extrapolates the logic of capitalist profit-seeking. If replacing workers with technology enables businesses to spend less on wages, and thus raise their profit margins and competitiveness, they will *have* to take every opportunity to automate. That is how market compulsion works. What this view lacks in subtlety, it makes up for with honesty. It may even be the dominant perspective among the automaters who publicly deny that their goal is to replace workers but confess in private meetings with tech consultants that they "crave the fat profit margins automation can deliver […] by letting them whittle departments with thousands of workers down to just a few dozen."[2]

If a machine learning algorithm were trained on Ford's prognostic method, it might discover the following pattern: he identifies entrepreneurs and companies that are working on a particular kind of automation, then predicts that they will soon perfect the technology, which will subsequently disseminate throughout and disrupt a given industry. A start-up is building a robotic arm that can quickly unload trucks; therefore, human warehouse workers are in deep trouble. Companies are designing automated restaurants; therefore, it is virtually inevitable that robots will soon cook our Big Macs and serve our lattes. These and other technologies will take over any job that is routine or predictable, whether it is blue- or white-collar.

But even if we grant Ford's point that the pursuit of profit drives capitalism, he makes two dubious assumptions. First, he takes for granted that the technologies he surveys can perform the work for which they have been designed. Second, he presumes that capitalist rationality dictates that as soon as a new cost-saving technology is operational, "rational business owners" will buy and employ it. The problem with the first assumption is that Ford reproduces advertising about tech products as if he were neutrally reporting on the state of the art in automation; the problem with the second is that Ford's immersion in ideologies of innovation blinds him to neoliberal capitalism's systemic weaknesses. Kim Moody observes that "the susceptibility of any job to automation is secondary to the potential profitability of its actual application" and to "the practicality of [its] application through actual investment."[3] Faced with an anemically growing economy, contemporary capitalists prefer to invest in Wall Street, not robots—to make money with money, not with new productive technology. Ford's image of a rational and robust capitalism is thus a mystified mirror that presents the system's impotence as its opposite. Like the meme of the cartoon dog who sips his coffee while his house burns down behind him, automation myths of the "rise of the robots" want to reassure us that "this is fine."

They were supposed to revolutionize manufacturing. Priced at $22,000–$29,000, they were allegedly poised to compete with low-wage labor overseas and help to bring factories back home. Whereas standard industrial robots can only blindly repeat the same tasks and are too dangerous to work alongside people, these new collaborative robots (cobots) were flexible, easy to train, and had machine vision that alerted them to nearby humans. These were no Terminators; their anthropomorphic eyes made them look "cute" and "disarmingly friendly."[4] Although a report on *60 Minutes* calculated that their average wage would be under $4 an hour, *Time* reassured readers that the cheap cobots were not a threat to workers since they only "perform low-level factory jobs, positions that are often menial, dangerous or undesirable."[5] Brynjolfsson and McAfee watched several of them at work "blowing past Moravec's paradox—sensing and manipulating lots of different objects with 'hands' ranging from grips to suction cups."[6] Equally impressed, Ford predicted that "we are, in all likelihood, at the leading edge of an explosive wave of innovation that will ultimately produce robots geared toward nearly every conceivable commercial, industrial, and consumer task."[7] Goldman Sachs and Amazon CEO Jeff Bezos were among several big-name investors.[8] But Baxter and Sawyer, the cobots created by Rethink Robotics, were failures. In October of 2018— just six years after unveiling Baxter—Rethink went out of business and sold its intellectual property, patents, and licenses to its distributor.

The hype around Baxter, Sawyer, and Rethink's co-founder Rodney Brooks, an AI superstar, was a prospective history that projected a linear model of technological change into the future. In the linear model, a technology that disseminates broadly and becomes a design norm—it "succeeds"— is retroactively posited as the teleological goal toward which all prior development led. To take a common example from science and technology studies: a linear model reads the history of the modern bicycle backwards from the "safety bicycle" created by Henry Lawson in the 1870s, as if the eventual success of Lawson's design were the key to understanding the history of bikes. As Wiebe E. Bijker states in a classic text in the field, "the focus on successful innovations suggests an underlying assumption that it is precisely the success of an artifact that offers some explanatory ground for the dynamics of its development."[9] This assumption obscures competing designs and the processes by which social groups came to understand and prefer the safety bicycle's affordances. Looking forward instead of backward, business sf about Baxter and Sawyer was a set of future histories that attempted to construct expectations around the fiction that the cobots were *already* the successful models from which subsequent robotics would unfold.

Rethink's short history is a lesson in the failure of an automation myth to shape markets. When Rethink released Baxter in 2012, Brooks stressed that the cobot was not intended to compete with traditional industrial robots. Those machines are large, fast, powerful, precise, difficult to program, and expensive; Baxter was slower, safer, more flexible, and cheaper. Rethink's target market were small manufacturers that do not use industrial robots because they change their production lines quickly and frequently, produce in relatively small, just-in-time batches, or cannot afford traditional robots or the costs of redesigning an entire production process around them. One of Brooks's guiding speculations was that the roughly 300,000 small manufacturers in the United States either already wanted a new kind of industrial robot or could be persuaded to want one.[10] The other was a modified techno-republicanism: Baxter was so cheap that it could substitute for outsourced Chinese factory labor and liberate the American worker to focus on more creative tasks.[11]

These speculations shaped Baxter's design. Instead of being programmed by an expert technician to repeat one task, Baxter could be trained and retrained by ordinary (American) workers for different tasks simply by moving its arms through the desired motions. In place of the expensive rigid motors that give traditional industrial robots their speed, power, and precision, Baxter was equipped with cheaper elastic actuators that enabled the cobot to use force sensing to feel its way through an environment and absorb impacts, thus minimizing potential harm to bystanders. When Ford and others predicted that Baxter, and later, Sawyer (the smaller, single-armed version of Baxter), were going to revolutionize robotics, they simply parroted Brooks's speculations that there was a large market demand for cobots with these specific abilities and that his company's products were capable of satisfying this demand. After all, when given a chance to save on labor costs, will business owners not jump to put a Baxter or two to work packing boxes or moving parts from one machine to another? And would not the chance to combine capitalist rationality with "Made in America" patriotism—Rethink's marketers stressed that the cobots were assembled in Massachusetts—make Baxter all but irresistible?

Almost six months after Baxter's release, Rethink still had not sold a single cobot. The writing was already on the wall when Chris Budnick, head of Vanguard Plastics in Southington, Connecticut, described Baxter as a "weakling" after Rethink gave him a demonstration of the cobot's unique selling points in early 2012. Burdick exemplifies Ford's rational capitalist: when Antonio Regalado of *MIT Technology Review* visited Vanguard in early 2013, he reported that Budnick displayed a tally of sales divided by work hours where all employees could see it. Budnick reasoned that the only way to stay in business was to raise productivity while maintaining or cutting hours. He was not interested in the "co-" aspect of cobots; he was willing to buy a Baxter only if it allowed him to fire an employee, and was so open about this desire that he even picked out said employee, a temp making $9 an hour, during his interview with Regalado: "'This will be a big test for [Rethink Robotics],' says Budnick, pointing to the tattooed worker stacking the cups. 'Because if they can't do that, what can they do?'"[12] A Rethink "Customer Success Story" on Vanguard's website indicates that Burdick eventually did buy one Baxter, but the concerns he raised about the cobot's weakness were common. Rethink failed because capitalist rationality in manufacturing still selects for strength, speed, repetition, and precision over ease of programming, flexibility, and patriotism.

On the one hand, Rethink's cobots did not work as advertised; on the other hand, in this context "work" means to satisfy owners' expectations of *strict control of the production process*. In the words of one of Rethink's former investors:

> What customers really want is a low-cost, simple, fast, repeatable robot. They want to put something in this exact location again, and again and

again. In the end, that was a lot more complicated for us to achieve than for some of our competitors because they weren't trying to do force sensing.[13]

What capitalists wanted from Baxter, in other words, was a better servant, a machine that could match and replace the disciplined, monotonous, degraded labor of the tattooed temp or the low-wage Chinese worker. Rethink's biggest competitors, such as Denmark's Universal Robots and Japan's Fanuc, have designed single-armed robots that are safe to operate next to human workers while still delivering speed and precision. They have no faces and will strike nobody as "cute," but they have sold far better than Baxter and Sawyer.

Where Baxter has flourished is in university labs and classrooms. By 2015, Rethink had sold only 1,000 cobots, a large portion of which went to universities. According to Brown University roboticist Stefanie Tellex, "everyone in robotics research today either has a Baxter or has a friend with a Baxter."[14] Business owners did not think Baxter's affordances increased control and accumulation, but researchers and students have found that the cobot's safety and ease of use are ideal for learning to program and studying human–robot interaction. Although academia is a key site of capitalist innovation, it is also still a place where slower, looser, non-pecuniary temporalities and social relations can thrive. This is the domain in which Rethink's cobots "work." That universities have become Baxter's home suggests not that Ford was incorrect to emphasize market rationality, but that his assessment of Baxter's economic impact was not capitalist *enough*. He mistook a technology that prospers in cooperative spaces on the edges of market domination for an ultra-capitalist technological fix.

Ford and other business futurists would probably respond that even though Rethink failed, some other company's robots will soon radically transform manufacturing. Statistics from the International Federation of Robotics (IFR), the industry's largest promotional organization, indicate that global industrial robot sales have set new records every year from 2012 to 2017. The IFR claims that the data show "a clear indication of the tremendous, accelerating rise in demand for industrial robots worldwide." But this hyperbolic ("tremendous") picture of a global upsurge looks different up close. Robot sales are not spread evenly across all industries but are instead concentrated in automotive and electrical/electronics. The IFR concedes that "the robot density in the general industry (all industries excluding automotive) is still comparatively low." Neither are all world regions buying robots at the same rate. Growing demand is driven largely by Asia, especially China, Japan, and Korea. Whereas robot installations in Asia averaged 25% annual growth between 2012 and 2017, the average annual growth rate was only 10% in the Americas and Europe during the same period.[15]

In the United States, most robots are concentrated in the automotive and manufacturing industries of Michigan, Ohio, Indiana, Tennessee, and a handful of other states in the Midwest and upper South. The entire western half of the United States employs only 13% of the nation's industrial robots, while the Detroit metropolitan area alone has more than three times the number of robots found in any other metro.[16] Moody emphasizes that

> the *only* industry with extensive use of robots globally as well as in the US is automobile manufacture—and that more than a half-century after their first introduction. [...] In other words, the introduction of robots has been both highly uneven and, for the most part, slow.[17]

While business sf fantasizes about waves of robots rapidly infiltrating all areas of the US economy, their numbers are in fact growing at modest rates, and they remain clustered in the geographic regions and industrial sectors in which they have been established for roughly the last 50 years.

One recent attempt to speed up the robotization of the automotive industry was a spectacular failure. Elon Musk, CEO of Tesla, tried to hyper-automate his factory in Fremont, California. Musk's vision of a "machine that builds the machine" was reminiscent of Cold War imaginaries of the fully automated factory: "You can't have people in the production line itself, otherwise you drop to people speed. So there will be no people in the production process itself. People will maintain the machines, upgrade them, and deal with anomalies." Ever the publicist, Musk took to social media to post videos of his production line and stoke the enthusiasm of Tesla's fanbase. Nonetheless, Tesla has consistently struggled to meet production targets for the Model 3. In early 2018, the Fremont factory made the highly unusual move of completely stopping its production line for a week. Musk conceded that automation at the factory was "excessive." A former GM executive was more pointed: "This shutdown is most likely for the purpose of ripping out all the '22nd century' fully-automated assembly systems which were going to 'revolutionize automotive manufacturing' and turned out not to work." The asset management firm AllianceBernstein claims that the factory's problems were in final assembly, where robots still can't "detect and account for threads that aren't straight, bolts that don't quite fit, fasteners that don't align or seals that have a defect."[18]

Musk's missteps suggest that even in their most advanced sector, robots are not marching ahead in droves and radically displacing human workers. Despite high levels of automation, total US employment in automotive/ automotive parts in January 2017 was nearly the same as it was in 1978, the year that set the industry's all-time employment record.[19] If robots have caused unemployment in recent decades, their effects have probably been concentrated in the metros with the most robots, leading some to speculate that anger over technological unemployment factored into Trump's 2016 electoral victories in the Midwest and Great Lakes. Yet technology is notoriously difficult to isolate as a cause of unemployment, especially since it can be accompanied by new labor-intensive tasks for which human workers are comparatively more reliable, cheaper, and more exploitable. Automation exists alongside, and can intensify, "heteromation," the extraction of surplus value from a heterogeneous array of cheap or free labor in digitally mediated networks.[20] Indeed, with a large, exploitable, low-wage, racially divided working class at their disposal, it is difficult to see why capitalists should feel the need to replace workers with robots.

Once we zoom back out from regional and industry-specific dynamics to systemic forces, we find that the story of the "rise of the robots" flies in the face of neoliberal capitalism's decades-long slump. The automation mythologists' *enfant terrible*, economist Robert Gordon, argues that the United States underwent a techno-economic revolution between 1870 and 1970. This "special century" was not only a period of robust economic growth but also qualitatively transformed some of the basic conditions of human life through the spread of electricity, the internal combustion engine, airplanes, indoor plumbing and heating, flush toilets, washing machines, cheap food, refrigerators, ready-made clothing, and antibiotics. Except for 1994–2004, the era of the internet's mass popularization, growth and productivity in the post-1970 period have been feeble. Technological change has clustered in entertainment, communication, and information processing and had less profound economic impacts. Dividing the years between 1870 and 2014 into three clusters (1870–1920, 1920–1970, 1970–2014), Gordon shows that per-person real GDP grew 1.8% and 2.4% per year in the first two periods, respectively, while labor productivity grew 1.7% and 2.8%, respectively. In the third period, GDP growth sank to 1.7% and labor productivity fell to 1.6%. Worse still, the trend growth in labor productivity fell to *zero* in 2013 and 2014. Such sluggishness helps to explain why companies have not deeply invested in new automation. In 2013, the ratio of net investment to capital stock was a mere 1%, down from the 3.2% average that characterizes the period between 1950 and 2007.[21]

Marxist critics' focus on declining and shifting profits complements Gordon's findings and the broad recognition among mainstream US economists that productivity growth has gone "missing."[22] Moody summarizes the Marxist view as follows:

> the mystery of [capitalism's] poor and declining performance lies in the volatility of the US and world-capitalist economies since the 1970s and the continuing problem of profitability. Profitability was not strong

enough and could not be sustained long enough under these circumstances to justify large and continuous investments in new technology.[23]

David Harvey argues that corporate profits migrated from manufacturing to financials in the 1990s because capitalists now prefer to invest in financial assets rather than production.[24] Or they invest in their own stock to drive up share prices: between 2015 and 2017, corporations spent nearly 60% of their profits on buybacks. This practice was further encouraged by the Trump tax cuts, which were ideologically pitched as a stimulant to business investment, but have been spent mostly on shares and dividends.[25] Outside of the financial industry, some of the largest US corporations generate profits not by revolutionizing production but through control of distribution and logistics (Walmart, Amazon), advertising (Google, Facebook), software rents (Microsoft), and branding (Apple). This is hardly an economy on the brink of a robot-driven explosion of productivity.

Capitalist stagnation distinguishes the post-2008 automation debate from the previous high-water mark of automation discourse in 1945–1970, the tail end of Gordon's special century. While representations of automation in popular culture tended toward pessimism and were part of a broader Cold War culture of dissent, automation myths were generally optimistic.[26] The technological dreams of an "affluent society" were buttressed by dynamic growth, the New Deal order's social contracts, and mobilization against communism. For the radical philosopher Herbert Marcuse, one of the era's greatest critics, liberation required the reinvention of critical negativity against a system that could "deliver the goods." But late neoliberal capitalism *cannot* deliver the goods. Viewed under the hard light of stagnation, today's robot futures are not only exaggerated, but perhaps even desperately blinkered. When Ford confronts Gordon's argument, his unwavering faith in innovation leads him to baldly assert that "it's impossible to imagine that such an immense increase in our overall computing capacity won't eventually have dramatic consequences in a variety of scientific and technical fields."[27] Unable to defend capitalism's record, Ford can only close his eyes and tells us what he cannot imagine—a world in which capitalism is technologically sluggish. Such is the fate of prophets of innovation whose gods are dead.

Notes

1 Ford, *Rise of the Robots*, 255–6.
2 Kevin Roose, "The Hidden Automation Agenda of the Davos Elite," *The New York Times*, January 25, 2019, www.nytimes.com/2019/01/25/technology/automation-davos-world-economic-forum.html.

3 Kim Moody, "High Tech, Low Growth: Robots and the Future of Work," *Historical Materialism*, 26, no. 4 (2018): 5.

4 Will Knight, "This Robot Could Transform Manufacturing," *MIT Technology Review*, September 18, 2012, www.technologyreview.com/s/429248/this-robot-could-transform-manufacturing/; John Markoff, "A Robot with a Reassuring Touch," *The New York Times*, September 18, 2012, nytimes.com/2012/09/18/sc ience/a-robot-with-a-delicate-touch.html.

5 Jack Linshi, "Meet Sawyer, a New Robot That Wants to Revolutionize Manufacturing," *Time*, March 19, 2015, https://time.com/3749307/rethink-ro botics-sawyer-robot/. Note how the headline reifies the robot as having its own desires.

6 Brynjolfsson and McAfee, *Second Machine Age*, 31. Moravec's paradox is that "it is comparatively easy to make computers exhibit adult level performance on intelligence tests or playing checkers, and difficult or impossible to give them the skills of a one-year-old when it comes to perception and mobility." Hans Moravec, *Mind Children: The Future of Robot and Human Intelligence* (Cambridge, MA: Harvard University Press, 1988), 15.

7 Ford, *Rise of the Robots*, 6.

8 Linshi, "Meet Sawyer"; Carol Lawrence, "Requiem for Rethink Robotics," *Mechanical Engineering*, February 2019, 44.

9 Wiebe E. Bijker, *Of Bicycles, Bakelites, and Bulbs: Toward a Theory of Socio-technical Change* (Cambridge, MA: MIT Press, 1997), 7. Similarly, Andrew Feenberg critiques what he calls "unilinear progress" in *Questioning Technology*, 77–8.

10 Rodney Brooks, "A New Class of Industrial Robot," Carnegie Mellon University, Robotics Institute, October 12, 2012, www.youtube.com/watch?v =RDvgNB2OZxI.

11 Atanasoski and Vora, *Surrogate Humanity*, 75–6.

12 I was puzzled by Regalado's seemingly gratuitous reference to the temp's tat-toos until I watched Rethink's "Customer Success Story." In the video, Budnick emphasizes that Vanguard is a family-owned business and that he considers his workers to be family. Surely he would not use technology to replace *family*? Although the cultural meaning of tattoos has changed in recent years, the temp's tattoos implicitly code them as a low-class, non-normative stepchild outside Vanguard's protected family circle.

13 Lawrence, "Requiem for Rethink Robotics," 42–3. Baxter's design has strong parallels to the failure of record-playback automation in the machine tools indus-try. See Noble, *Forces of Production*, 84–5.

14 Steven Crowe, "Inside the Rethink Robotics Shutdown," *The Robot Report*, November 13, 2018, www.therobotreport.com/rethink-robotics-shutdown.

15 International Federation of Robotics, *Executive Summary World Robotics 2018 Industrial Robots*, www.ifr.org/downloads/press2018/Executive_Summary_WR _2018_Industrial_Robots.pdf. In another instance of his speculative method, Ford reports that the iPhone assembler Foxconn is planning to add 1 million robots, then takes this as evidence that Foxconn will soon be a giant automated factory. Foxconn made the announcement in 2012. It immediately fell far behind schedule. See Ziyi Tang and Tripti Lahiri, "Here's How the Plan to Replace the Humans Who Make iPhones with Bots is Going," *Quartz*, June 22, 2018, https:/ /qz.com/1312079/iphone-maker-foxconn-is-churning-out-foxbots-to-replace-its -human-workers/.

16 Mark Munro, "Where the Robots Are," *The Avenue* (blog), The Brookings Institution, August 14, 2017, www.brookings.edu/blog/the-avenue/2017/08/14/where-the-robots-are/.

17 Moody, "High-Tech, Low Growth," 8–9.

18 Jeffrey Rothfeder, "Elon Musk Has Delivery Problems," *The New Yorker*, January 10, 2017, www.newyorker.com/business/currency/elon-musk-has-delivery-issues; Russ Mitchell, "Musk Has Second Thoughts on Aggressive Automation for Tesla Model 3," *Los Angeles Times*, April 17, 2018, www.latimes.com/business/autos/la-fi-hy-tesla-model-3-20180417-story.html; Helen Edwards and Dave Edwards, "How Tesla 'Shot Itself in the Foot' by Trying to Hyper-Automate Its Factory," *Quartz*, May 1, 2018, https://qz.com/1261214/how-exactly-tesla-shot-itself-in-the-foot-by-trying-to-hyper-automate-its-factory/.

19 Moody, "High-Tech, Low Growth," 9.

20 Daron Acemoglu, and Pascual Restrepo, "Jobs and Robots: Evidence from US Labor Markets," *NBER Working Paper Series 23285*, National Bureau of Economic Research, March 2017, www.nber.org/papers/w23285; Daron Acemoglu, and Pascual Restrepo, "Artificial Intelligence, Automation, and Work," *NBER Working Paper Series 24196*, National Bureau of Economic Research, January 2018, www.nber.org/papers/w24196; Munro, "Where the Robots Are"; Mike Davis, "The Great God Trump & the White Working Class," *Catalyst* 1, no. 1 (2017): 151–71. Hamid R. Ekbia, and Bonnie A. Nardi, *Heteromation, and Other Stories of Computing and Capitalism* (Cambridge, MA: MIT Press, 2017).

21 Robert J. Gordon, *The Rise and Fall of American Growth: The U.S. Standard of Living Since the Civil War* (Princeton, NJ: Princeton University Press, 2016), 14, 327, 585–9.

22 Moody, "High-Tech, Low Growth," 23; Robert Brenner, *The Economics of Global Turbulence: The Advanced Capitalist Economies from Long Boom to Long Downturn, 1945–2005* (London: Verso, 2006); Michael Roberts, *The Long Depression: Marxism and the Global Crisis of Capitalism* (Chicago, IL: Haymarket Books, 2016). The University of Chicago Booth School of Business asked a panel of leading economists whether "missing productivity growth" was due to the mismeasurement of the relevant data. Thirty-seven percent disagreed or strongly disagreed, 37% were uncertain, and a mere 7% agreed. Nobody strongly agreed. "Missing Productivity Growth," IGM Forum, February 15, 2018, www.igmchicago.org/surveys/missing-productivity-growth.

23 Moody, "High-Tech, Low Growth," 26. See also Benanav, "Automation and the Future of Work—1" and "Automation and the Future of Work—2."

24 David Harvey, *The Enigma of Capital and the Crises of Capitalism* (Oxford, UK: Oxford University Press, 2010), 21–3.

25 Katy Milani, and Irene Tung, "Curbing Stock Buybacks: A Crucial Step to Raising Worker Pay and Reducing Inequality," The Roosevelt Institute, July 31, 2018, https://rooseveltinstitute.org/curbing-stock-buybacks-crucial-step/; Annie Lowrey, "Are Stock Buybacks Starving the Economy?" *The Atlantic*, July 31, 2018, www.theatlantic.com/ideas/archive/2018/07/are-stock-buybacks-starving-the-economy/566387/.

26 On the culture of dissent, see Margot A. Henriksen, *Dr. Strangelove's America: Society and Culture in the Atomic Age* (Berkeley, CA: University of California Press, 1997). Bix calls the period the "era of automation triumphant." Bix, *Inventing Ourselves*, 250.

27 Ford, *Rise of the Robots*, 68.

7   Amazon, or Automated Taylorism

Visitors to the Amazon Robotics website are greeted with a video of a small fleet of "drive units" gliding through a warehouse. In most shots, the cavernous warehouse looks eerily posthuman. As the squat, boxy, Roomba-like robots carry stacks of bins with no people in sight, they seem to be propelled by a will of their own and by a knowledge of the warehouse's layout that none of the human workers possesses—or needs. A few human workers make a brief appearance as the robots deliver bins for them to scan and sort, but they are stationary and unimpressive. They are neither the video's subject matter nor its addressees. The text overlay that encourages the visitor to apply for jobs at Amazon's newly expanded "innovation hub" in Westborough, Massachusetts, is obviously not intended for these appendages of the machine. Their job is to execute the work conceived for them by the robots' designers, the Westborough engineers and managers whom the visitor is invited to join—provided one has the proper credentials and is invested in the ideologies of innovation.[1]

Like Elon Musk's vision of a fully automated Tesla plant, the Amazon Robotics video solicits expectations of a more efficient, rational, post-labor future. Some business sf writers have swallowed the bait. In a widely cited article that was published several months after Amazon acquired Kiva Systems, the start-up that had produced the drive units before being absorbed into Amazon Robotics, Carl Benedikt Frey and Michael A. Osborne speculate that logistics workers are at the forefront of a whopping 47% of total US employment that is at "high risk" for automation.[2] Martin Ford believes that the drive units and other robots "will eventually displace a lot of people in [Amazon] warehouses."[3] But while the Amazon Robotics video pitches this automation myth to prospective tech professionals, the company has worked hard to dispel concerns that it will replace workers with technology. *Day One*, Amazon's corporate blog, stresses that "approximately 300,000 full-time jobs have been added globally" since the introduction of drive units in

2012. Not only does automation at Amazon "disprov[e] the misconception that machines are replacing humans in the workforce," it *improves* jobs while growing them: "robotic animation benefits employees, as they take over performance of fulfillment centers' less desirable, more tedious tasks." Robots aren't replacements, they're "dance partners."[4]

Although Amazon has a huge R&D budget and is certainly using it to explore more ways to "liberate" labor from warehouses, the most labor-intensive task, picking, continues to resist automation. Brad Porter, Amazon's Vice President of robotics, admits that "the current state of the art is not capable of handling the diversity of Amazon's product selection."[5] Eight years after purchasing Kiva Systems, only about 15% of Amazon warehouses use drive units.[6] The director of Amazon Robotics Fulfillment has suggested that the fully automated warehouse is at least a decade away.[7] Business sf often uses the unit of "a decade or so" to express vague faith that a technology will eventually arrive. To my ear, the expression means little more than "someday, somehow." It is a statement of desire, not of fact.

The task of technoclastic thinking is to break the horns of the dilemma between business sf's dystopia of joblessness and its public relations utopia of human–robot "dancing." These are two sides of the same coin. They both assume that automation is about technically replicating workers' skills, and both are deterministically convinced that such "progress" is relentlessly marching ahead. The two positions differ only on the question of whether this progress replaces or complements current workers. Spellbound by a fantasy image of sheer technical feasibility, "engineering bottlenecks,"[8] and the natural laws of capitalist development, they ignore the wide range of factors that limit warehouse automation. These include managerial wariness toward large capital investments in an industry with narrow profit margins, especially when significant capital has already been invested in older warehouse technologies that are still operational; the relative cheapness of outsourcing and temp labor; the difficulty of rapidly adjusting automated systems to unpredictable changes in consumer demand; and the incompatibility between a warehouse's architecture and the space requirements of new technologies.[9]

A much less flattering perspective is that capitalism's technological progress is typified by automation that helps management make *control of the human workforce* more automatic, more opaque to workers, and more destructive of their skills and general wellbeing. Automation does so not by expelling workers from their jobs and creating a pristinely posthuman and rationalized workplace. The rise of online shopping led to a 37% growth in warehouse employment between 2014 and 2017, and further growth is expected.[10] Automation is transforming what these growing jobs entail, how an enlarged pool of workers accomplishes tasks, and the exact amount of time they are allotted to do so. The most plausible outcome of automation in the warehouse industry is not the disappearance of jobs but their further material and moral degradation.[11]

In his seminal critique of Taylorism in *Labor and Monopoly Capital: The Degradation of Work in the Twentieth Century* (1974), Harry Braverman argues that scientific management breaks the unity of conception and execution in workers' minds and bodies.[12] In the early days of scientific management, the separation of ideas of how work should be done (conception) from their embodied performance (execution) relied on management's analog study of what we might call the working class's algorithms of work—the "recipes" of work, to use a common contemporary metaphor for algorithms. With the aid of close observation, the stopwatch, and the time–motion study, scientific managers gained knowledge of work processes that were embedded in workers' skills and traditions and strengthened workers' power in the workplace. Scientific managers then translated worker knowledges into procedures that served as a template for new work processes that they broke down into discrete, repetitive, mindless steps that management could dictate to unskilled, low-wage workers. The intended result was not only increased productivity and the cheapening of labor and its products but greater managerial control over the content, conditions, and pace of work. While preserving the fundamentals of these older techniques, Amazon has updated Taylorism by delegating management's control of conception and execution to digital systems that surveil workers and subject them to algorithmic routines. In other words, the work of management itself—the task of studying, reconstituting, and controlling the work process—has been partially automated. If Frederick W. Taylor, the so-called father of scientific management, could be teleported to the present, he would immediately recognize in Amazon's system his own principles in an automated form.[13]

The work process in an Amazon warehouse is an enormous assemblage that links warehouse workers of various kinds to the warehouse's technical objects and systems, other warehouses, delivery drivers, the Amazon website, consumers, and myriad other actors and systems that are too numerous to list. Thus, I will focus on a portion of that assemblage that most directly shapes the experiences of pickers in warehouses without drive units (which are the large majority of warehouses). An Amazon picker's workday is organized around an innovation that is far less technologically sexy than an autonomous mobile robot: a handheld scanner. The scanner displays the location of an item and counts down the seconds remaining for the worker to locate, scan, and place the item in a bin. Workers must keep up a furious pace and walk several miles a day, risking physical injury and mental stress, to ensure that they scan all items on time and "make rate." The scanner tracks workers' location and must always be carried, even during bathroom breaks. A middle manager enthusiastically told journalist Emily Guendelsberger, who worked as a temp for Amazon in 2015 and has written one of the richest first-person accounts of the company's secretive work conditions, that the warehouse is essentially a panopticon: "Amazon knows how your day is spent. [...] *There's always an eye out there on you.*"[14]

The scanner not only subjects workers to continuous surveillance but also assures that they exercise the least amount of judgment. Shortly after starting her job as a picker, Guendelsberger became little more than a set of reflex movements: "I don't really need to think at all. All I need to do is keep walking."[15] Pickers hardly need to think because the work process has been fragmented into monotonous tasks that they must complete faster than the speed of reflection. Decisions about conception and execution are controlled by the scanner, the opaque algorithmic network that determines what, how, and when work is to be done, the engineers and managers who design and maintain this network, and behind them all, the whole hurly-burly of market domination (a condition that Amazon ideologically frames as a cult-like devotion to consumers).[16] When Guendelsberger momentarily gains a vantage point over the warehouse as a whole, the scene is almost ineffable: "the shelves abruptly end in a breathtaking panoramic view of the rest of SDF8, which somehow looks even more vast from this high vantage point. I spend a few minutes of Time Off Task gazing through the safety bars at all the ant-like workers below going about their mysterious jobs."[17] Guendelsberger's inability to grasp the totality of the "mysterious" work process isn't a mere intellectual failure on her part; it is the material effect of a management-defined "fair day's work," implemented through fragmentary steps and an impersonal binary logic of on-time/late. The "safety bars" through which she gazes might as well be prison bars guarding the work process from worker understanding.

In a letter that addresses allegations by a plaintiff who claims to have been fired for complaining about productivity quotas, an Amazon lawyer has provided one of the more detailed glimpses into the black box of Amazon's automated Taylorism:

> In order to ensure that associates are processing orders as efficiently as possible, Amazon developed a proprietary productivity metric for measuring and weighting productivity of each associate. The metric system is used at all North American fulfilment centers and sets forth a standardized metric based on several weeks of quality performance data across North America. The productivity rate is also based on a metric applied at all North American fulfillment centers and is evaluated quarterly to make modifications as necessary.
>
> Each Wednesday, facilities hold quality and productivity performance reviews to review data from the prior week. In order to measure

performance fairly and consistently, metrics are reviewed across the entire building. While managers can provide feedback on productivity rates for their respective departments, the productivity rate is the same for every associate during the timeframe reviewed. Any determination to modify productivity rates is made by mangers [sic] outside the facility. Importantly, individual site managers do not have the ability to set or manipulate production rates, and rates are based on purely objective goals.

Amazon's system tracks the rates of each individual associate's productivity and automatically generates any warnings or terminations regarding quality or productivity without input from supervisors. [...] While managers have no control over rates, they can override the automatically-generated notices in order to exempt or override the notice if a policy was applied incorrectly.[18]

The lawyer's account confirms what many Amazon workers have experienced on the warehouse floor. They are monitored by an automated "productivity metric" that treats them not as individuals but as data points. What is remarkable is that this system's automaticity is even unaccountable to on-site managers, whose work appears to be digitally Taylorized as well. These managers use the metric to review their underlings' performance, but they cannot exercise judgment about the metric itself. The metric is set by a shadowy group of managers "outside the facility" and by the automation mythologist's favorite *raison d'etre* for eliminating human decision-making: "purely objective goals."

Neither are local managers responsible for automatically generated warnings and firings, which they can only override after the fact. The lawyer reveals elsewhere in the same letter that "hundreds" of employees at a Baltimore warehouse were fired between August 2017 and September 2018 for failing to make rate. *The Verge* journalist Colin Lecher estimates that, given the warehouse's number of full-time employees, about 10% of the total workforce in Baltimore is fired annually for falling short of productivity metrics. This amounts to thousands of workers a year when extrapolated across all Amazon warehouses in the United States.[19] The icing on the lawyer's cake of rationalizations is the claim that the system's automaticity proves its fairness, and thus disproves the plaintiff's allegations.

Amazon spokespeople tend to respond to critiques of warehouse working conditions by pointing to workers' relatively high wages and benefits. For Guendelsberger, pay is not the main reason that Amazon jobs are bad. It's "the unrelenting emphasis on 'making rate,' or hitting your daily individual productivity goals, paired with the company's uncanny ability to monitor workers in real time."[20] Workers state that the relatively high pay is not worth it "if you don't like being a complete robot." They claim that working at

Amazon "makes you feel absolutely downtrodden." It's "soul-sucking" and "dehumanizing."[21] Pain, chronic injury, depression, and crying on the job are commonplace. Some workers faint; others die.[22] Those who learn to cope with aches and anxiety are faced with boredom and the loneliness that seems to be engineered into the way the algorithm ensures that pickers rarely cross one another. These are the job's true wages, the brutalities that accumulate when workers lose meaningful decisions over the conception and execution of their labor. And since Latinx and black workers are the majority of the US warehouse workforce,[23] they shoulder a disproportionately heavy load of the surveillance and alienation that pervade low-wage America.

Warehouses are way stations for the circulation of commodities; their function is to get the goods, store them, and direct them toward purchasers.[24] While the manufacturers whose products flow through warehouses have seen sluggish productivity growth for several decades, Amazon and its workforce are rapidly expanding. The company's market success hinges on increasing the speed of circulation. Amazon's automation is fundamentally oriented toward bending the minds and bodies of an expanding human labor force to the inhuman pace of commodities in motion. By focusing too much attention on technological unemployment and platitudes about human–machine collaboration, Amazon's robots—not to mention its more speculative delivery drones—are a distraction from the more significant effect that the company's technology is having on warehouse labor: the robotization of living labor. Drawing on Marx's characterization of productive technology as the embodiment of dead or past labor, Braverman remarks that "the ideal toward which capitalism strives is the domination of dead labor over living labor."[25] At Amazon, the dead ideas of those whose "science" consists in the control of labor are more grotesquely vivacious than ever.

Notes

1   The video is available at https://amazonrobotics.com.
2   Carl Benedikt Frey, and Michael A. Osborne, "The Future of Employment: How Susceptible are Jobs to Computerisation?" (Working paper, Oxford Martin Programme on Technology and Employment, University of Oxford, 2013).
3   Nick Wingfield, "As Amazon Pushes Forward with Robots, Workers Find New Roles," *New York Times*, September 10, 2017, www.nytimes.com/2017/09/10/technology/amazon-robots-workers.html. To be more precise, Amazon's "robots" encompass three different quantities and types: 100,000 drive units; 30 "palletizers," robot arms that stack bins on pallets for shipping or stowing; and 6 "robo-stows," another kind of robot arm that places pallets on drive units. See "What Robots Do (and Don't Do) at Amazon Fulfilment Centers," *Day One* (blog), https://blog.aboutamazon.com/innovation/bots-by-the-numbers-facts-and-figures-about-robotics-at-amazon.

4   "Bots by the Numbers: Facts and Figures about Robotics at Amazon," *Day One* (blog), December 18, 2018, https://blog.aboutamazon.com/innovation/bots-by-th e-numbers-facts-and-figures-about-robotics-at-amazon.

5   Rich Blake, "Amazon's Push to Augment Workforce with Automation is Pig in Industrial Robotics Python," *Forbes*, February 24, 2019, www.forbes.com/sites /richblake1/2019/02/24/amazons-push-to-augment-workforce-with-automation -is-pig-in-industrial-robotics-python/.

6   "Bots by the Numbers."

7   Nandita Bose, "Amazon Dismisses Idea Automation will Eliminate all its Warehouse Jobs Soon," *Reuters*, May 1, 2019, www.reuters.com/article/us-ama zon-com-warehouse/amazon-dismisses-idea-automation-will-eliminate-all-its-w arehouse-jobs-soon-idUSKCN1S74B9.

8   Frey and Osborne, "The Future of Employment," 26.

9   Beth Gutelius, and Nik Theodore, "The Future of Warehouse Work: Technological Change in the U.S. Logistics Industry" (UC Berkeley Labor Center; Working Partnerships USA, October 2019), 37–41, 43–4, http://laborcenter.berkeley.edu/ future-of-warehouse-work/.

10   Gutelius and Theodore, "The Future of Warehouse Work," 15.

11   This is the thesis of Gutelius and Theodore's "The Future of Warehouse Work."

12   Harry Braverman, *Labor and Monopoly Capital: The Degradation of Work in the Twentieth Century* (New York: Monthly Review Press, 1974), 78–9.

13   "Amazon's shop-floor processes are an extreme variant of Taylorism that Frederick Winslow Taylor himself, a near century after his death, would have no trouble recognizing." Simon Head, *Mindless: Why Smarter Machines Are Making Dumber Humans* (New York: Basic Books, 2014), 36. A related concept in the literature is algorithmic management. See Min Kyung Lee, Daniel Kusbit, Evan Metsky, and Laura Dabbish, "Working with Machines: The Impact of Algorithmic and Data-Driven Management on Human Workers," *Proceedings of the 33rd Annual ACM Conference on Human Factors in Computing Systems* (2015): 1603. For a recent study that builds directly on Braverman and work process theory, see Katherine C. Kellogg, Melissa Valentine, and Angele Christin, "Algorithms at Work: The New Contested Terrain of Control," *Academy of Management Annals* 14, no. 1 (2020), https://journals.aom.org/doi/10.5465/ann als.2018.0174.

14   Emily Guendelsberger, *On the Clock: What Low-Wage Work Did to Me and How It Drives America Insane* (New York: Little, Brown and Company, 2019), 35.

15   Guendelsberger, *On the Clock*, 48.

16   On Amazon's quasi-religion of the consumer, see Head, *Mindless*, 37.

17   Guendelsberger, *On the Clock*, 48–9.

18   This document was obtained by the tech news website *The Verge* through a Freedom of Information request. See Colin Lecher, "How Amazon Automatically Tracks and Fires Warehouse Workers for 'Productivity,'" *The Verge*, April 25, 2019, www.theverge.com/2019/4/25/18516004/amazon-warehouse-fulfillment-centers-productivity-firing-terminations. The document from which I quote is hosted at https://cdn.vox-cdn.com/uploads/chorus_asset/file/16190209/amazon _terminations_documents.pdf.

19   Lecher, "How Amazon Automatically Tracks and Fires."

20   Guendelsberger, *On the Clock*, 22.

21   Guendelsberger, 22.

22 Dave Jamieson, "The Life and Death of an Amazon Warehouse Temp," *Huffington Post*, https://highline.huffingtonpost.com/articles/en/life-and-death-amazon-temp/.
23 Gutelius and Theodore, "The Future of Warehouse Work," 23–4.
24 Edna Bonacich, and Jake B. Wilson, *Getting the Goods: Ports, Labor, and the Logistics Revolution* (Ithaca, NY: Cornell University Press, 2008); Moody, *On New Terrain*, chap. 5.
25 Braverman, *Labor and Monopoly Capital*, 157.

8   Uber is a Science Fiction

Since its founding in 2009, the ride-hailing company Uber has been devoted to making its workers disappear. Like other "gig economy" platforms, Uber misclassifies workers as independent contractors to circumvent labor laws. The message to drivers on the Uber website is the language of entrepreneurial independence: "You can drive when you want, where you want, and how you want"; "there's no office and no boss"; "with Uber, you're in charge."[1] But since even entrepreneurs can be said to work, Uber has also attempted to remove drivers from the realm of work altogether, first rhetorically, then technically. In response to a lawsuit filed in 2013, an Uber lawyer claimed that drivers and passengers are essentially the same, since both are "customers" to whom Uber licenses its app for a fee.[2] When Uber began testing its self-driving cars in Pittsburg in 2016, the company simply tried to take its anti-worker strategies to the next level. Having invisiblized workers through legal and ideological means, Uber is now attempting to make them disappear through automation. Uber's quest to create an autonomous taxi service is not a "disruption" of transportation but a pristine example of how automation myths grow fat on the disavowal of living labor.

Like Amazon, Uber manages labor algorithmically, delegating a large portion of the analysis and administration of work's conception and execution to opaque, panoptical software. Uber collects a wealth of data about drivers, including their location, speed, the smoothness or roughness with which they brake, the rate at which they accept and decline ride requests, their total number of trips, customer ratings, and even audio and video from inside the vehicle.[3] Algorithms use this data to dictate to drivers the who, what, when, and how of their labor—whom to pick up and when and where to do so, what route to take to passengers' destinations, how to drive while getting there, etc. Uber also determines whether drivers may continue to drive; those who refuse too many rides, or whose customer ratings fall below the algorithmically monitored threshold, run the risk of being locked out of the Uber app, i.e., fired.

This control is the contradiction at the heart of the company's misclassification of drivers. Technology ethnographer Alex Rosenblat argues convincingly that Uber's refusal of its employer status cannot be squared with the fact that its "dispatching practice, app design, and penalty system all shape how [drivers] are required to behave at work."[4] Thus, what makes Uber's algorithmic management so different from Amazon's is that Amazon acknowledges that it is an *employer* managing *workers*. Amazon has no interest in pretending that the warehouse workers who are subject to its productivity metrics are actually self-employed entrepreneurs (though the company is *very* interested in shifting responsibility for part-time workers to temp agencies).[5] Because Uber is thoroughly committed to this fiction—its existence in a historically low-profit industry may depend on it—the company's control of conception and execution assumes a contradictory form. The algorithms must manage labor without appearing to manage labor.

If Taylor is automated in Amazon's algorithm, perhaps Bill Lumbergh is the ghost in Uber's machine. In a famous scene in the anti-work classic *Office Space* (1999), Lumbergh uses a hilariously pseudo-friendly, passive-aggressive communication style to force his hapless employee Peter to work on the weekend:

> Hello, Peter. Whaaat's happening? Ummm, I'm gonna need you to go ahead and come in tomorrow. [...] Mmm, 'k? Oh! And I almost forgot [...] uhh, I'm also gonna need you to go ahead and come in on Sunday, too. 'Kay?

Lumbergh represents the absurd circuitousness of managerial power trying not to be managerial power. Lumbergh constantly beats around the bush—wonderfully captured by his verbosity and elongated vowels and "mm"s—and unconvincingly disguises himself as a friend who is simply making casual requests. Given that Lumbergh manages a software company and is a graduate of MIT, it does not seem too far-fetched to imagine him in Silicon Valley, his voice echoing in the Uber app's insinuations. One Uber driver in Chicago describes the app's suggestions as follows: "It was all day long, every day—texts, emails, pop-ups: 'Hey, the morning rush has started. Get to this area, that's where demand is biggest.'" Another driver in Tampa, Florida tried to log out only to receive the following message: "You're $10 away from $330 in net earnings. Are you sure you want to go offline?"[6] Uber uses these and similar prompts to keep drivers working and generating value for the company, but since they are only notifications and are worded as casual Lumberghian requests ("Hey") and suggestions ("Are you sure?"), Uber denies that they constitute an employer's control of employees. Yet as Rosenblat observes, these "nudges" set expectations and are difficult for drivers to disregard. Combined with the rating system, they help Uber produce a standardized consumer experience while threatening drivers who don't comply with potential deactivation from the app.[7] In the end, Peter knows full well that Lumbergh is still a boss.

As Uber continues to try to make workers disappear in court, where it is battling a number of pro-worker rulings,[8] its second front is automated driving. While the self-driving car has a long speculative history,[9] business sf usually identifies the DARPA (Defense Advanced Research Projects Agency) Grand Challenge of 2004 as the "crucial innovation," the moment of transition from "science fiction to everyday reality."[10] No autonomous vehicles were able to complete the Challenge, a 150-mile race through the Mojave Desert, but five completed the course in the following year. Six vehicles finished the 2007 DARPA Urban Challenge. What business sf likes about this story is its neat linearity, the movement from failure to ever-higher stages of success, propelled by engineering genius, entrepreneurial pluck, and Moore's Law.

By the time Uber's self-driving cars began shuttling a small number of pre-selected passengers around downtown Pittsburgh, the events of the Challenge years had solidified into a robust automation myth. Whereas driving had once been a paradigm case of tacit knowledge, an intuitive human algorithm that could never be translated into a computer's explicit code, the new self-driving cars proved the old theories wrong.[11] They might not think like human drivers, but with enough sensors and computing power, self-driving cars could surpass human proficiency. Once the measure of skilled driving, humans were now the monkey wrench in the transportation system, the cause of traffic jams and inefficient use of city space for parking lots. "When you need [a car]," one prominent business futurist has speculated,

> you will simply call for it as you might for a taxi today, but it will appear much more reliably and promptly. [...] Within a few decades, you will no more consider purchasing your own car than you would think today of buying a private railroad coach.[12]

But the most frequently cited and apparently unimpeachable business sf rationale for self-driving cars is safety. Uber's former CEO Travis Kalanick has predicted that once driving becomes an automated, app-mediated service, "a million fewer people are going to die a year. Traffic in all cities will be gone. Significantly reduced pollution and trillions of hours will be given back to people."[13] President Obama repeated Kalanick's main points when he weighed in on Uber's experiment for the *Pittsburgh Post-Gazette:* "Automated vehicles have the potential to save tens of thousands of lives each year. [...] Safer, more accessible driving. Less congested, less polluted roads. That's what harnessing technology for good can look like."[14] Waymo, which began as the Google Self-Driving Car Project, begins the "Mission" section of its website with a large picture of a father and child, the implied victims of the current automobile system, and claims that 94% of crashes in the United States involve human error.[15] Perhaps the most zealous proponent of the safety argument is Elon Musk, in whose hands automation myths mutate from sales pitches to sheer gaslighting. In Musk's mind, technoclasm is nothing less than murder: "If, in writing some article that's negative you effectively dissuade people from using an autonomous vehicle, you're killing people."[16]

Myths of autonomous driving have been instrumental in shaping the future expectations of some municipal and state governments. These have helped to create the deregulated political and social environments that allow business sf to indulge its fantasies of unstoppable technological progress, which in turn further strengthens tech companies' power to shape future expectations. Pittsburgh's mayor Bill Peduto was a model technological determinist when he welcomed Uber's self-driving experiment to his city. "It's not our role to throw up regulations or limit companies like Uber," the mayor explained to his constituents, who had not voted on the matter. "You can either put up red tape or roll out the red carpet. If you want to be a 21st-century laboratory for technology, you put out the carpet."[17] Peduto's rationalizations reflect the neoliberal public policy that has shaped Pittsburgh's rebirth as a tech and innovation hub after deindustrialization and the decline of the Steel City.[18] In this "business-friendly" regime, the ideal function of government is to negate itself as much as possible—except when tech companies need regulators to retool laws to meet their needs, as when Peduto helped to defeat a statewide ban on ride sharing in 2014. Is it surprising, then, that Uber has often been flippant toward the law and has rebranded illegality as bold entrepreneurial "disruption"? Shortly after Peduto endorsed the company, Uber left California because its unabashed defiance of the state's permit requirements forced a confrontation with the Department of Motor Vehicles. Echoing Peduto, Arizona governor Doug Ducey welcomed Uber to his more business-friendly state with open arms: "This is what OVER-regulation looks like! #ditchcalifornia."[19]

What is truly remarkable is that even with the aid of neoliberal policy, self-driving technology still falls short of expectations. The Society of Automotive Engineers distinguishes among six levels of autonomy, from no automation (L0) to full automation (L5), defined by an automated system's capacity to drive "everywhere in all conditions" without human intervention.[20] Most of the "self-driving" cars that have made the headlines in recent years are low-level, partially automated systems that require a human driver and function only in particular environments and circumstances. Neither

Uber, Waymo, nor any other company currently offers self-driving services outside of a few small pilot programs. Tesla's Autopilot technology is classified as L2 semi-automation that requires the driver to continuously scan the environment and maintain readiness to assume control at any moment.[21] Over a decade after the DARPA Urban Challenge, the most advanced self-driving technology still cannot manage bad weather, poorly maintained roads, or the unpredictable behaviors of human drivers and pedestrians. "We overestimated the arrival of autonomous vehicles," admits Ford's chief executive Jim Hackett.[22]

One reason that the self-driving hype bubble has popped was the death of an Arizona woman after being struck by a computer-controlled Uber car in 2018. Forced to suspend Uber's self-driving experiments after the crash, Ducey must have recognized that he had put his foot in his mouth when he gloated about California's "over-regulation." An investigation by the National Transportation Safety Board concluded that "the self-driving system software classified the pedestrian as an unknown object, as a vehicle, and then as a bicycle with varying expectations of future travel path." By the time the car's technology determined that emergency braking was necessary, it was too late to avoid a collision. A human driver was behind the wheel, but she was watching her smartphone during the crucial seconds leading up to the collision and pressed the brakes only after the pedestrian had been hit.[23]

Perhaps the Uber driver was motivated by the same faith in automation that had killed Joshua Brown when his Tesla Model S drove into a tractor-trailer in 2016. A Tesla blog post stated that Autopilot failed to distinguish the white tractor-trailer from the brightly lit sky, and emphasized that Autopilot only assists human drivers who must keep their hands on the wheel at all times. But why name a technology "Autopilot" if it is not actually an autopilot? "The moment the first driver took to the roads in a car running Autopilot," writes urbanist Adam Greenfield, "a gulf opened up between what the function could actually do and its implicit premise—a premise underwritten by everything from Musk's public commentary to Tesla's choice of naming."[24] Although the branding was different, the Uber driver who was looking at her phone while the car barreled toward the pedestrian may have fallen into this same gap between automation and fauxtomation.

The safety advantages of self-driving cars over human-driven cars are a radical speculation that business sf naturalizes as fact. Once we depart from the technochauvinistic assumption that computers are a priori more reliable than humans, how can we really *know* that computers can drive more safely than people? Tech companies usually point to their internal figures on the number of test miles that their cars have driven. Even if we take their word on the accuracy of these figures, most of the test miles have probably been produced in limited and specific environments that cannot compare to the complex environments that human drivers face daily. When Waymo announced that it had accumulated 4 million miles of self-driving, its map showed that these miles had been logged only in Washington, California, Arizona, and Texas, comfortably removed from the realities of snow. It is also unclear how many of the miles were generated on self-driving cars' easiest obstacle course, well-marked highways.[25] In any event, claims about test driving are thoroughly speculative. In 2013, there were 1.09 fatalities per 100 million miles driven by humans. Now imagine that Uber wanted to demonstrate that 100 self-driving cars can achieve a fatality rate just 20% safer than human driving. This probably would not be enough to convince a skeptical US population,[26] but let us assume it is. In our hypothetical scenario, Uber also wants to prove this safer rate with 95% confidence and 80% power (i.e., the probability of correctly avoiding false positives and false negatives). To provide statistically relevant results, Uber would have to test drive the cars 24 hours a day, 365 days a year, at an average speed of 25 miles per hour, *for half a millennium*. If Uber wanted to lower the rate of improvement to just 5%, it would have to drive for *ten millennia* since very similar rates between self-driving and human-driven cars would require additional evidence to show that their difference is statistically significant. The RAND Corporation study that calculates these figures concludes that "developers of this technology and third-party testers cannot drive their way to safety."[27] When Kalanick said self-driving cars will save "millions" of lives, he was effectively asking us to pretend that we are already living in Uber's future, no matter its dissonances with the actual present. In other words, he was requesting a 500- to 10,000-year benefit of the doubt.

A similar fudging underlies the almost universally cited statistic that 94% of crashes are due to human error. When Uber first announced its Pittsburgh experiment, the company blog stated that "self-driving cars have the potential to save millions of lives and improve quality of life for people around the world. 1.3 million people die every year in car accidents—94% of those accidents involve human error."[28] To the untrained ear, this seems to say that human error is the *cause* of 94% of car accidents. But the sources from which Uber and others construct the "potential" of automated driving draw a more nuanced conclusion. The National Motor Vehicle Crash Causation Survey stresses that while drivers can be identified as the "critical reason" for a "pre-crash event," the concept of critical reason does not necessarily identify "the cause of the crash [or] imply the assignment of fault to a vehicle, driver, or environment, in particular."[29]

Uber is a science fiction. It uses counter-factual arguments to orient expectations around claims that drivers aren't workers, that regulatory laws don't exist, and that self-driving cars can manage the hazards of the road in ways that are clearly superior to human drivers. As Uber prepared to go public in early 2019, Rosenblat described how Uber consistently conceals what it *is* behind what the company would like the public to believe it *will be*: "Uber's main PR pitch for its $120 billion valuation is that it's not an unprofitable ridehail company. It's actually a self-driving car company and the future Amazon of transportation." "I find this ask," Rosenblat continues in a follow-up tweet, "for people to ignore what it is, and to believe what it can become—fascinating. Because I've seen this play for years. It should be a broadway show."[30] For all Uber's song and dance, however, there is a persistent social vision that connects the pivots and reversals. Whether alleging to be a software-licensing company or a self-driving car service, whether using algorithms to manage labor with maximum plausible deniability or trying to engineer labor's technical obsolescence, the root speculation is that driving labor doesn't exist. For Uber, the world consists solely of platform owners, engineers, anti-regulation policy makers, consumers, and technologies that facilitate their market transactions. In the contemporary fascination with self-driving cars, it is this neoliberal utopia that is striving for automaticity.

Notes

1 See uber.com/signup/drive/.
2 Alex Rosenblat, *Uberland: How Algorithms are Rewriting the Rules of Work* (Oakland, CA: University of California Press, 2018), 4.
3 Rosenblat, *Uberland*, chap. 5; Andrew Beinstein and Ted Sumers, "How Uber Engineering Increases Safe Driving with Telematics," *Uber Engineering* (Blog), June 29, 2016, https://eng.uber.com/telematics/; Mareike Möhlmann and Ola Henfridsson, "What People Hate About Being Managed by Algorithms, According to a Study of Uber Drivers," *Harvard Business Review*, August 30, 2019, https://hbr.org/2019/08/what-people-hate-about-being-managed-by-algorithms-according-to-a-study-of-uber-drivers; Kate Conger, "Uber Embraces Videotaping Rides, Raising Privacy Concerns," *New York Times*, November 20, 2019, www.nytimes.com/2019/11/20/technology/uber-recording-rides-privacy.html.
4 Rosenblat, *Uberland*, 95.
5 Where Amazon and Uber most clearly converge is in Amazon's app-mediated delivery driver platform Amazon Flex, which is essentially Amazon's version of Uber.
6 Noam Schreiber, "How Uber Uses Psychological Tricks to Push Its Drivers' Buttons," *The New York Times*, April 2, 2017, www.nytimes.com/interactive/2017/04/02/technology/uber-drivers-psychological-tricks.html.
7 Rosenblat, *Uberland*, 150.
8 In late 2018, a UK Court of Appeal upheld a prior ruling that Uber drivers are workers and thus subject to laws that regulate minimum wages and holiday pay. The judgment highlighted "the air of contrivance and artificiality which pervades Uber's case." In 2020, California Assembly Bill 5, popularly known as the "gig" law, went into effect. The bill stipulates that "a person providing labor or services for remuneration shall be considered an employee rather than an independent

contractor unless the hiring entity demonstrates that the person is free from the control and direction of the hiring entity in connection with the performance of the work." Sandra Fredman and Darcy Du Toit, "One Small Step Towards Decent Work: Uber v Aslam in the Court of Appeal," *Industrial Law Journal* 48, no. 2 (2019): 272. https://leginfo.legislature.ca.gov/faces/billTextClient.xhtml?bill_id =201920200AB5.

 9 See Dan Albert, *Are We There Yet?: The American Automobile Past, Present, and Driverless* (New York: Norton, 2019).

10 John Markoff, "Google Cars Drive Themselves, in Traffic," *The New York Times*, October 10, 2010, www.nytimes.com/2010/10/10/science/10google.html; Ford, *Rise of the Robots*, 181.

11 Brynjolfsson and McAfee, *Second Machine Age*, 16–20.

12 Kaplan, *Humans Need Not Apply*, 195.

13 Travis Kalanick, interview with Biz Carson, *Business Insider*, August 18, 2016, www.businessinsider.com/travis-kalanick-interview-on-self-driving-cars-future -driver-jobs-2016-8?op=1.

14 Barack Obama, "Barack Obama: Self-driving, Yes, but also Safe," *Pittsburgh Post-Gazette*, September 20, 2016, www.post-gazette.com/opinion/Op-Ed/2016/ 09/19/Barack-Obama-Self-driving-yes-but-also-safe/stories/201609200027.

15 See https://waymo.com/mission/.

16 Albert, *Are We There Yet?* 265.

17 Cecilia Kang, "No Driver? Bring It On. How Pittsburgh Became Uber's Testing Ground," *The New York Times*, September 10, 2016, www.nytimes.com/2016/09 /11/technology/no-driver-bring-it-on-how-pittsburgh-became-ubers-testing-grou nd.html.

18 Allen Dieterich-Ward, *Beyond Rust: Metropolitan Pittsburgh and the Fate of Industrial America* (University of Pennsylvania Press, 2015), 199–230.

19 Rosenblat, *Uberland*, 173–5; Carolyn Said, "Uber Puts the Brakes on Testing Robot Cars in California after Arizona Fatality," *San Francisco Chronicle*, March 27, 2018, www.sfchronicle.com/business/article/Uber-pulls-out-of-all-self-d riving-car-testing-in-12785490.php.

20 A graphic of the most recent version of the schema can be found at www.sae.org /news/2019/01/sae-updates-j3016-automated-driving-graphic.

21 J. Shutko, B. Osafo-Yeboah, C. Rockwell, and M. Palmer, "Driver Behavior While Operating Partially Automated Systems: Tesla Autopilot Case Study," SAE Technical Paper 2018-01-0497, 2018, https://doi.org/10.4271/2018-01 -0497.

22 Neal E. Boudette, "Despite High Hopes, Self-Driving Cars Are 'Way in the Future,'" *New York Times*, July 17, 2019, www.nytimes.com/2019/07/17/bus iness/self-driving-autonomous-cars.html.

23 "Preliminary Report Released for Crash Involving Pedestrian, Uber Technologies, Inc., Test Vehicle," National Transportation Safety Board Office of Public Affairs, May 24, 2018, www.ntsb.gov/news/press-releases/Pages/NR20180524. aspx; "'Inadequate Safety Culture' Contributed to Uber Automated Test Vehicle Crash—NTSB Calls for Federal Review Process for Automated Vehicle Testing on Public Roads," National Transportation Safety Board Office of Public Affairs, November 19, 2019, www.ntsb.gov/news/press-releases/Pages/NR20191119c .aspx.

24 Adam Greenfield, *Radical Technologies: The Design of Everyday Life* (London: Verso, 2018), 224.

25 "Waymo's Fleet Reaches 4 Million Self-Driven Miles," *Medium*, November 27, 2017, https://medium.com/waymo/waymos-fleet-reaches-4-million-self-driven-miles-b28f32de495a.

26 The majority of Americans would not want to ride in a self-driving car if given the chance. John Gramlich, "Americans Had Concerns about Self-driving Cars before Fatal Arizona Accident," Pew Research Center, March 21, 2018, www.pewresearch.org/fact-tank/2018/03/21/americans-had-concerns-about-self-driving-cars-before-fatal-arizona-accident/.

27 Nidhi Kalra, and Susan M. Paddock, "Driving to Safety: How Many Miles of Driving Would It Take to Demonstrate Autonomous Vehicle Reliability?" RAND Corporation, 2016, www.rand.org/pubs/research_reports/RR1478.html. Uber's 2018 safety report cites the RAND study and shares its conclusion that test driving "require[s] an impractical magnitude of driving exposure." This finding has not stopped Uber representatives from using test statistics to persuade the public that self-driving cars are safer. See Uber Advanced Technologies Group, "A Principled Approach to Safety," 2018, https://uber.app.box.com/v/UberATGSafetyReport.

28 "Steel City's New Wheels," *Uber Blog*, May 19, 2016, www.uber.com/blog/pennsylvania/new-wheels/.

29 Albert, *Are We There Yet?* 265–7.

30 Alex Rosenblat, Twitter post, January 23, 2019, 5:00pm, https://twitter.com/mawnikr/status/1088104286565863429.

9   The Smart Home

Still More Work for Mother

The protagonist of Ray Bradbury's short story "There Will Come Soft Rains" (1950) is a fully automated house—a "smart home," as it would be marketed today. Published in the midst of the Cold War and America's second automation debate, Bradbury's story imagines that the house has survived the death of its inhabitants in a nuclear war in 1985.[1] But the home is not so smart after all, for it pointlessly repeats its services for a bygone family: it makes eggs, toast, and coffee for breakfast; issues reminders that school and work are about to start; readies the car; washes the dishes; vacuums; cleans up after the family dog; organizes games and entertainment in the nursery; prepares and cleans up dinner; draws a bath; lights an evening cigar. Bradbury describes the house as "an altar with ten thousand attendants, big, small, servicing, attending, in choirs." After the "gods had gone away," the "ritual of the religion continued senselessly, uselessly."[2] But what, exactly, is the "religion" of home automation?

By speculatively subtracting human life from an automated environment, Bradbury invites readers to inquire about the forms of life that are programmed to repeat in this environment. Bradbury's story can be read as an exercise in what political theorist Langdon Winner terms "epistemological Luddism," a compatriot of technoclasm that Winner defines as a method for learning about technologies through purposeful withdrawal. By destabilizing a technology's smooth functioning in everyday life, the epistemological Luddite can gain new perspectives on how the selected technology shapes consciousness and behavior: "prominent structures of apparatus, technique, and organization would be, temporarily at least, disconnected and made unworkable in order to provide the opportunity to learn what they are doing for or to mankind."[3] Bradbury employs Winner's method in reverse; instead of removing technology, he eliminates people from a technical system. The effect is to render the technical system—and the "ritual of the religion"— pointless. The pointless, in turn, raises the question of the original point or purpose.

In "There Will Come Soft Rains," the analysis of technology's purpose must go beyond Winner's undifferentiated "mankind." For the "senseless" and "useless" house indicates the senses and uses of automation for the gendered labors of social reproduction. According to social reproduction theory, capitalism cannot persist across generations without the production and reproduction of life itself—the labors of sheltering, feeding, caring for, and socializing people. Social reproduction encompasses the work of "birthing and socializing the young," "caring for the old, maintaining households and family members, building communities, and sustaining the shared meanings, affective dispositions, and horizons of value that underpin social cooperation."⁴ While much socially reproductive labor takes place in schools and hospitals, the home is its epicenter, the heteronormative, patriarchal family is its dominant mode of organization, and unpaid mothers and wives are its main providers. Bradbury's story imagines that the automated production and reproduction of human life in the home has become conspicuously absurd in the absence of people. Bradbury explicitly genders the house, ascribing to it an "old-maidenly preoccupation with self-protection."⁵ Yet the description is somewhat gratuitous because the house's scheduling, cooking, cleaning, and childcare are precisely the tasks expected of women. This is what haunts Bradbury's posthuman world—not the Promethean hubris of humanity as such but the automation of gendered labor. It is easier to imagine the end of the world than the end of women's work.

For all its utility as speculative Luddism, Bradbury's story badly misreads the trajectory of domestic technosocial relations in the early post-World War II period. Bradbury's automated house flies in the face of Ruth Schwartz Cowan's famous thesis in *More Work For Mother*: although household technologies such as running water, toilets, central heating, gas and electric stoves, refrigerators, and washing machines spread broadly across class divides after the war, raising household productivity and reducing housework's physical burden, they did not significantly reduce the overall amount of time women spent in domestic labor. While Bradbury invites his Cold War readers to imagine that houses will be fully automated within 30 years, Cowan shows that women's work never came close to disappearing. Instead, during this period mothers and housewives worked just as much as their mothers and grandmothers, if not more. Why? Cowan identifies several causes, including higher standards of cleanliness and food variety, a decline in the availability of paid domestic servants—or more precisely, this job shifted from white women to immigrant and US-born women of color—and ideologies of domesticity that constructed solitary housework as proof of women's familial love. "There is more work for a mother to do in a modern home because there is no one left to help her with it."⁶ Bradbury's house is gendered female because it is simply the exteriorization and routinization of dominant technosocial relations and gender ideologies. The house is an ultra-mother, single-handedly commanding a battery of technologies to complete the tasks expected of the individual housewife with her stove, washing machine, and vacuum, but without her fatigue or stress or "problem that has no name."[7]

While smart homes still cannot fry an egg for breakfast, today's myths of home automation still echo the promise of Bradbury's house: an integrated experience of comfort, security, and entertainment, all achieved through technologies that operate according to an ideological image of perfect motherhood and housewifery. *Time* journalist Patrick Lucas Austin updates Bradbury's tale in the following speculation about the smart home of 2029:

> It's 6 A.M., and the alarm clock is buzzing earlier than usual. It's not a malfunction: the smart clock scanned your schedule and adjusted because you've got that big presentation first thing in the morning. Your shower automatically turns on and warms to your preferred 103°F. The electric car is ready to go, charged by the solar panels or wind turbine on your roof. When you get home later, there's an unexpected package waiting, delivered by drone. You open it to find cold medicine. Turns out, health sensors embedded in your bathroom detected signs of an impending illness and placed an order automatically.[8]

Austin goes on to cite "experts"—that is, business sf writers—who predict that in about ten years, smart homes will be seamless AI environments. An assemblage of networked software, sensors, and interfaces will track your music preferences and automatically play your favorites songs, dim the lights around the time you usually go to bed, activate your Roomba vacuum, and operate your kitchen's knife-wielding robot chef. Tony Fadell, who was CEO of Nest Labs before it became Google Nest in 2014, describes the smart home as an environment in which artificial cognition gathers information from smart devices and uses the data to anticipate user desires before users articulate them: "the home [...] is aware of what your family is doing and tries to help you. [...] It should be all these little touchpoints that make your life simpler."[9] Whether waking you up for work or putting you to bed, bathing you or warding off your cold, cooking your meals or vacuuming up your crumbs, the smart home is a "nest," a space in which life is nurtured by artificial mothers. This automation myth is perhaps most fully realized in Amazon's digital assistant Alexa, which can connect to Amazon's smart home devices and the online retailer's vast catalog. (When AI is supposed to signify intellect, it is given male names like Watson; when it is supposed to signify care, it is given female names like Alexa.) "Alexa, order laundry detergent," "Alexa, start the coffee maker," "Alexa, turn the temperature down"—in such commands, "Alexa" neatly substitutes for "Mom," a husband's pet name for his wife, or the moniker of a paid domestic servant.

Despite its continuities with Bradbury's speculation, today's smart home finds itself in a different historical conjuncture. Fadell's and Amazon's vision of home automation represents one of the dominant technological fixes for the contemporary crisis of social reproduction. Expressed in popular consciousness as "burnout" and the feeling that one never has enough time, the crisis is materially rooted in neoliberal capitalism's divestment from social welfare and its transfer of ever more social reproduction from public services to privatized individuals, families, and communities. These latter are in turn struggling to provide adequate socially reproductive labor under the pressures of non-unionized, low-wage, precarious jobs, dual-income families, and debt.[10] There was more work for Cowan's mothers because no one was left to help them with it, but many mothers were not yet juggling social reproduction and wage labor because their husbands' wages were sufficient to provide for the entire family. From 1970, the period that ends Cowan's history, to 2016, dual-income income couples with children under 18 rose from 49% to 66% of American families.[11] Men now do more housework than their fathers and grandfathers, but women still do nearly twice as much as men even while their participation in the wage labor force has grown considerably.[12] When today's working mothers find time for themselves between their jobs and unpaid labor at home, this time is more frequently interrupted, fragmented, and mixed with childcare than men's leisure time.[13]

The smart home's "solution" to the crisis of social reproduction is the transformation of the home into a complete technological commodity, an intelligent network that monitors and manages life and meets as many socially reproductive needs as possible through automated purchases. "The clear aim of such 'smart home' efforts," writes Adam Greenfield, "is to as nearly as possible short-circuit the process of reflection that stands between one's recognition of a desire and its fulfillment via the market."[14] Working parents can come home to groceries already ordered and delivered by Alexa, carpets vacuumed by a Roomba, family meals prepared by the robot chef, and children monitored by smart watches and entertained by Netflix. Women are "liberated" from labor that they now order and command as paying customers, and the home itself sloughs off its oppressive history and emerges as a space of equal exchange and contract.

This vision of the smart home is perhaps the most radical automation myth of all because it speculates that the labor of life-making, which is larger than and underpins wage labor, can be completely brought into the orbit of the capitalist market. The political philosopher Nancy Fraser has claimed that capitalism "free-rides" on "activities of provisioning, caregiving, and interaction that produce and maintain social bonds, although it accords them no monetized value and treats them as if they were free." Fraser characterizes the relation between activities that capitalism recognizes as economically valuable and social reproduction as "separation-*cum*-dependence-*cum*-disavowal."[15] But in the smart home, social reproduction becomes a commodity like any other, and capitalism's hidden and disavowed condition of possibility is smoothly integrated into it—*for paying customers*. In other words, the smart home's "solution" to the crisis of social reproduction simply assumes that the crisis has already been solved, and that Americans who are currently working insecure jobs while providing for elderly family members and helping kids with homework have magically acquired the means to pay for the homes, devices, apps, and subscription services that will free them. In fact, many of these same Americans are the very warehouse workers, delivery drivers, retail workers, and fast food workers whose exploited labor is hidden behind the smart home's fauxtomatic processes. They are the ones making and delivering the goods ordered by Alexa, not the ones receiving them. They are the disproportionately African American and Latinx working class whose homes were foreclosed in 2007–2009.

The gendered division of socially reproductive labor is the religion of the smart home, the perfection of women's servitude its ritual. But a society that installs oppressive gender norms in technology is unlikely to overcome this oppression with the same technology. Thus, even for those who can pay, the smart home will probably not replace women's work but once again raise cleanliness standards, strengthen the ideologies of middle-class motherhood, and create more work for mother. In fact, when smart home ads show what women will do once they have been liberated from domestic drudgery, they usually cannot imagine an alternative to gendered social reproduction. For example, a commercial for the Roomba 980 depicts a housewife in a large, spacious house.[16] Even though the woman is beaming as she watches her toddler crawl on a spotless carpet and hardwood floors—she is the epitome of domestic bliss—the female voiceover acknowledges that maintaining a sanitary environment for growing children is demanding: "Keeping your home beautifully clean every day is hard but important work." The woman touches a button on her smartphone and delegates some of this work to her Roomba, which appears to clean the house by itself. Of course we don't see all the non-automated work that robot vacuums require: users must prepare rooms for automated vacuuming by creating uncluttered paths for the robot's movements, monitor the vacuum and free it when it gets stuck in curtains, periodically clean the vacuum's filters and dispose of waste, and remove messes that the vacuum itself creates (such as when it vacuums and spreads pet feces). In many homes, robot vacuums do not replace traditional vacuuming but add to it.

And what does the woman in the commercial do with the imaginary free time created by ignoring the labor that is necessary for automated processes to function smoothly? She teaches her daughter to fold laundry.

Notes

1 The year has been pushed back in subsequent editions. In the Harper Perennial Modern Classics edition cited below, the story is dated August 2057.

2 Ray Bradbury, *The Martian Chronicles* (New York: Harper Perennial Modern Classics, 2011), 250.

3 Langdon Winner, *Autonomous Technology: Technics-out-of-Control as a Theme in Political Thought* (Cambridge, MA: MIT Press, 1977), 330.

4 Nancy Fraser, "Crisis of Care? On the Social-Reproductive Contradictions of Contemporary Capitalism," in *Social Reproduction Theory: Remapping Class, Recentering Oppression*, ed. Tithi Bhattacharya (London: Pluto, 2017), 23. Bhattacharya's introduction to this volume provides a lucid mapping of contemporary social reproduction theory. For a classic text in the field, see Lise Vogel, *Marxism and the Oppression of Women: Toward a Unitary Theory*, rev. ed. (1983; repr., Leiden, the Netherlands: Brill, 2013).

5 Bradbury, *Martian Chronicles*, 250.

6 Cowan, *More Work For Mother*, 201. On the transformation of the domestic labor force, see Mignon Duffy, *Making Care Count: A Century of Gender, Race, and Paid Care Work* (New Brunswick, NJ: Rutgers University Press, 2011), chap. 2.

7 On "the problem that has no name," see Betty Friedan, *The Feminine Mystique*, 50th anniversary ed. (1963; repr., New York: Norton, 2013).

8 Patrick Lucas Austin, "What Will Smart Homes Look Like 10 Years from Now?" *Time*, July 25, 2019, https://time.com/5634791/smart-homes-future/.

9 Matt Vella, "Nest CEO Tony Fadell on the Future of the Smart Home," *Time*, June 26, 2014, https://time.com/2926418/nest-ceo-tony-fadell-on-the-future-of -the-smart-home/.

10 Fraser, "Crisis of Care?" 32–5.

11 Gretchen Livingston and Kim Parker, "8 Facts about American Dads," *Fact Tank: News in the Numbers*, Pew Research Center, June 12, 2019, www.pewresearch.org/fact-tank/2019/06/12/fathers-day-facts/.

12 "American Time Use Survey," U.S. Bureau of Labor Statistics, December 20, 2016, www.bls.gov/tus/charts/household.htm. Men's housework clusters around food/drink preparation and yard work, while cleaning bathrooms and doing laundry largely remain women's work.

13 Judy Wajcman, *Pressed for Time*, 81.

14 Greenfield, *Radical Technologies*, 36.

15 Fraser, "Crisis of Care?" 24.

16 Watch the commercial here: www.youtube.com/watch?v=tZ0bq-jIg-o.

10   Care Robots

To complete its fantasy of totally automated social reproduction, the smart home requires additional technologies. Sensors can automatically adjust a thermostat but cannot help an elderly person put on a sweater. Alexa can order groceries but cannot assist someone into and out of the bathtub. A Roomba can remove dust but cannot serve a glass of water to soothe a late-night cough. When business sf dreams of technically closing the circle of life-making, it imagines robot caregivers.

The case for care robots appears to be a simple matter of supply and demand. People are living longer and shifting global demographics. A 2015 report by the US Census predicts that the world population of people aged 65 and over will have increased by 1.6 billion in 2050, a growth of 150% over 2015 levels. In contrast, the world population of people under 20 will remain roughly the same as it is today, while the population of working-age people will shrink as a percentage of total population due to lower fertility rates. The United Nations report "World Population Prospects" predicts that in 2100, the United States will have the youngest median age (45.5) among the rapidly aging G7 nations—Japan and Italy will have the oldest median ages (53.8 and 53.4, respectively)—but the US will still be older on average than the rest of the world.[1] Who will care for the elderly in this gray future? It seems to be a straightforward problem of arithmetic. There simply will not be enough young and working-age people to attend to the new legions of seniors.

The scarcity of care is the guiding premise of Louise Aronson's *New York Times* op-ed "The Future of Robot Caregivers" (2014). Aronson, a geriatrician, describes a house call that just won't end. Her patient holds her hand, tells her rambling stories, and slowly shuffles with her walker in search of special objects to show the doctor. The disabled elderly woman is lonely but the busy Aronson has no more time to give her. The patient's daughter lives far away, and the caregivers and friends who occasionally check in on her do not seem to be enough. Aronson presents this particular shortage of people and time as a microcosm of the bigger problem: "we do not have anywhere near enough human caregivers for the growing number of older Americans." What this elderly patient and others like her need, Aronson proposes, "is someone who is always there, who can help with everyday tasks, who will listen and smile": "a robot caregiver." Switching into full-on business sf mode, Aronson speculates about the future of caregiver robotics as if reporting a fact: "in the next decade, robot caregiver prototypes will become much more sophisticated." Aronson imagines a robot that is always "alert and available in case of crisis," does laundry while her patient sleeps, speaks to her "with a kind, humanlike voice," helps her get out of bed and use the toilet, reminds her to take medication, and even "chat[s] with her about the weather or news." The robot could make her patient smile, which is something that the woman probably rarely does now, "when she's home alone, hour after hour and day after day."[2]

Aronson admits that there are alternatives to robot caregivers but is far less imaginative about them. While she indulges myths of evermore sophisticated "robot caregiver prototypes"—there is currently no robot that comes close to performing all the tasks Aronson imagines[3]—she refuses to think beyond the present when it comes to an "ideal" world in which "each of us would have at least one kind and fully capable human caregiver to meet our physical and emotional needs as we age." Aronson quickly dismisses this possibility: "most of us don't live in an ideal world." True enough. But neither do we live in the ideal world of robot caregivers that can fold laundry and discuss the news. Why does this reality invite speculative transcendence and the sustained attention of an op-ed while the one centered on the expansion of human care does not? Aronson seems to find it easier to imagine a technological fix to elderly care, unproven technology be damned, than to imagine a shift in how elderly care is socially organized. Perhaps this is because of how Aronson portrays the people who currently provide elderly home care in the United States:

> Almost always it is 24/7 and unpaid or low wage, and has profound adverse health consequences for those who do it. It is women's work and immigrants' work, and it is work that many people either can't or simply won't do.

In other words, robots are the more plausible solution to the scarcity of care because they seem to be detours around the political problem of exploited, gendered, and immigrant labor.[4]

Elderly care can be understood theoretically as the portion of socially reproductive labor that maintains the retired, disabled, or chronically ill members of the non-working population. If childcare is the social reproduction of a future generation of workers, elderly care is the social reproduction of a previous generation of waged and unwaged workers and older people who otherwise do not work. What is at stake in elderly care is the question of how to socialize the maintenance of life for people who, due to retirement, disability, or sickness, do not sell their labor power for a wage and are not recognized as economically productive members of the polity.[5] In the United States, this question has been answered in a peculiar way: elderly care is distributed primarily as welfare, financed and administered by a hybrid public–private health care system, and produced by a low-wage workforce that consists of a disproportionately high number of US-born and immigrant women of color.

Historians Eileen Boris and Jennifer Klein show that modern home care was created by the New Deal welfare state as paid work relief for women on public assistance, most of whom were African American women with experience in domestic service. The New Deal legacy is a social organization of care in which federal welfare funds are used by state and local governments and private contractors to pay "undeserving," poor, racialized women to care for the "deserving" elderly, chronically ill, and disabled.[6] According to a study of over 4 million workers in the formal and informal long-term care sector, today roughly 86% of workers are female, 26% are African American (nearly double the black population's percentage of the total US population), and 23% are naturalized, legal noncitizen, or unauthorized immigrants (predominantly from Mexico, the Philippines, Jamaica, Haiti, and the Dominican Republic). Other studies of home health aides, personal care aides, and nursing assistants have shown that the workforce consists mostly of part-time workers who earn about $19,000 annually and experience high rates of poverty. The color line divides the workforce internally as well; while nearly all are working class and working poor, women of color earn lower hourly wages than white women in home care, residential care, and nursing homes.[7]

This social organization of home care, created by the welfare state and maintained by racialized public–private labor markets and immigration policies, has become so entrenched and naturalized that many take for granted that meeting the needs of patients is possible only on the backs of a servile and invisible class of poor whites and racialized and immigrant women. The Great Recession and the ensuing budget crises hardened these assumptions. Starting from the premise of fiscal crisis, attempts to improve working conditions and expand care inevitably become battles over spending and "big government," deservingness and undeservingness, "Americans" and "foreigners." And yet for all their labors, home care workers are the Uber drivers of the health care industry. They must constantly battle both the devaluation of their work and arguments like that of the conservative National Right to Work Legal Defense Foundation, which has claimed in court that home care workers are not workers but "providers [who] are simply a group of citizens who receive monies from a government program."[8]

No wonder, then, that the science fiction of care robots appears to be a plausible way to reform home care. It reiterates the techno-republican dream not of abolishing servitude, which would require systemic political change, but of perfecting it by technical means; not of recognizing and respecting the labor of women and racialized others, but of robotically simulating it.[9] What takes the form of a simple supply-and-demand problem is in truth a mystified expression of political choices about the social value of elderly life beyond the wage labor market, about whose labor counts as fully human, and about who gets to be a member of the American community.[10] The true scarcity is not of supply but of political imagination and will. The fact is that there are already millions of US-born and immigrant workers caring for elderly Americans and many more who would be willing and able to do so if only home care were treated as work befitting human dignity and belonging. Is this an "ideal"? Yes—a sounder and more just one than the myth of robot caregivers.[11]

If advocates for care robots are concerned about shortages of care labor, the far right recognizes the abundance of potential caregivers but dangerously misperceives it as "white genocide." A neglected motivation behind the white supremacist terrorist attack in El Paso, Texas, on August 3, 2019 was the perpetrator's racialized anxieties about automation. The killer's online manifesto reveals that he was a firm believer in business sf and had consigned himself to becoming technologically unemployed. He combined this techno-pessimism with anxieties about climate change, the irreversible destruction of the natural environment by corporations and hyper-consumption, and resource scarcity.[12] What catalyzed the technological and environmental crises in the killer's mind was his paranoia that Latinx hordes, aided by "open border" policies, were overrunning the United States and replacing whites through immigration and high birth rates. His solution was to spark a race war that he hoped would compel Latinxs to leave the country. This would not only reduce the population's strain on natural resources but also allow the low-wage, low-skill jobs filled by US-born and immigrant Latinxs (such as home care) to be automated, which would then block any further need for this racialized labor in the United States. What most automation mythologists never say publicly but often pursue in practice—they would like technology to control and displace as much low-wage, gendered, and racialized human labor as possible—the El Paso shooter stated bluntly and murderously.[13]

Although the shooter took pains to explain that his views preceded the presidency of Donald Trump, they resonate deeply with far-right movements that hail Trump as a white leader. They are even characteristic of certain elements of Trumpism itself. To name only some of the most egregious examples: the terrorist who went on a shooting spree at two mosques in New Zealand—and who directly influenced the El Paso terrorist—celebrated Trump as a "renewed symbol of white identity." The *Washington Post* has found that counties that hosted a Trump campaign rally in 2016 witnessed a 226% spike in hate crimes.[14] When Trump has spoken directly about white supremacy, he has either dismissed evidence that it is a growing problem or effectively exonerated it, as when he infamously walked back his rebuke of the murder of a leftist counter-protestor by a white supremacist at the 2017 Unite the Right rally in Charlottesville, Virginia and instead blamed "both sides." None of this should be surprising, however, given that Trump's ban on immigrants from Muslim-majority countries and his project to build a wall along the US–Mexico border are cornerstones of Trumpism and contemporary white nationalist nativism. Among the many translators between the movements is senior Trump advisor Stephen Miller, who has promoted "white genocide" literature online and was instrumental in conceiving the Muslim Ban and the brutal policy of family separation at the US–Mexico border.[15] Though Trump has not explicitly connected automation and immigration, Trumpism's nativist politics easily snap into place when combined with racist automation myths.

I do not intend to equate Aronson's advocacy for robot caregivers and far right nativism. Ignoring home care workers, preferring to dream of technological fixes, naively assuming that automation simply complements workers instead of deteriorating their working conditions—these are not equivalent to calling for further automation to help whiten America. But as Daniel Denvir shows in *All-American Nativism: How the War on Immigrants Explains Politics as We Know It* (2020), liberals and conservatives have long shared the assumption that authorized and unauthorized non-European immigration is a "problem": a drain on public services, a racial and cultural invasion, a threat to native workers and wages, a national security issue, an affront to legal immigrants who enter the country the "right way," or, in Trump's words, an influx of "criminals" and "rapists." Denvir's thesis is that Trump, for all his antics, is not an exception to normal American politics but the culmination of a deeply entrenched tradition of nativism. Liberals remain firmly in this tradition whenever they accept its terms, as they do when they oppose the family separation policy while assuring constituents of their dedication to addressing "border security."

The myth of care robots can play too easily into this framework. The ascendance of white nationalism requires an explicit defense of the rights of racialized and immigrant workers in general and home care workers in particular, a radically expanded and more hospitable concept of American community, and unequivocal rejection of the techno-republican desire for automated servitude.

As an imaginary solution to the real contradictions of home care, the robot caregiver embodies a failure to recognize the non-machines who are already caring for America. In the words of Boris and Klein, "revaluing what is integral to the labor, establishing the legitimacy of care as productive and necessary labor, represents a recognition that would require redefining worth and remuneration across the whole economy."[16] The care robot skirts this labor of redefinition. It represents its advocates' inability to imagine care for all who need it, provided by well-remunerated human workers who are accepted as full members of the polity. This is one of the aims of technoclasm: to show that the gee-whiz technologies for which we appear to be destined are boringly unimaginative.

Notes

1 Wan He, Daniel Goodkind, and Paul Kowal, *An Aging World: 2015* (Washington, DC: U.S. Government Publishing Office, 2016), 3–5; Christine Tamir, "G7 Nations Stand Out for their Low Birth Rates, Aging Populations," Pew Research Center, August 23, 2019, www.pewresearch.org/fact-tank/2019/08/23/g7-nations-stand-out-for-their-low-birth-rates-aging-populations/.
2 Louise Aronson, "The Future of Robot Caregivers," *The New York Times*, July 19, 2014, www.nytimes.com/2014/07/20/opinion/sunday/the-future-of-robot-caregivers.html.
3 Most existing technologies are therapeutic, such as Paro the robot seal, or single-function, such as the patient-lifting Robear. Even Martin Ford is skeptical: "an affordable, multitasking elder-care robot that can autonomously assist people who are almost completely dependent on others probably remains far in the future." Ford, *Rise of the Robots*, 156.
4 Aronson, "The Future of Robot Caregivers." To be fair, while her op-ed has the dubious honor of exemplifying the mythology of care robots, Aronson is more measured and critical of heath care technology in her subsequent book *Elderhood: Redefining Medicine, Life, and Aging in America* (New York: Bloomsbury, 2019).
5 These formulations have been influenced by Serap Saritas Oran's social reproduction theory of pensions. See Serap Saritas Oran, "Pensions and Social Reproduction," in *Social Reproduction Theory*, 148–70.
6 Eileen Boris and Jennifer Klein, *Caring for America: Home Health Workers in the Shadow of the Welfare State* (Oxford, UK: Oxford University Press, 2012).
7 Leah Zallman, Karen E. Finnegan, David U. Himmelstein, Sharon Touw, and Steffie Woolhandler, "Care for America's Elderly and Disabled People Relies on Immigrant Labor," *Health Affairs* 38, no. 6 (2019): 919–26. Robert Espinoza, "Immigrants and the Direct Care Workforce," *PHI*, June 2017, https://phinational.org/wp-content/uploads/2017/06/Immigrants-and-the-Direct-Care-Workforce-PHI-June-2017.pdf; Kezia Scales, "It's Time to Care: A Detailed Profile of America's Direct Care Workforce," *PHI*, January 21, 2020, https://phinational.org/resource/its-time-to-care-a-detailed-profile-of-americas-direct-care-workforce/.

8   Boris and Klein, *Caring for America*, 220–1.
9   Almost no one has openly advocated for totally automating care and replacing human caregivers with robots. But neither has Rethink Robotics, Amazon, or Uber stated that its goal is to replace workers.
10 Boris and Klein, *Caring for America*, 224.
11 To be sure, immigration alone is not a silver bullet that magically solves population aging. As soon as we accept the mathematical framework in which the "shortage" is represented, as soon as we try to calculate the number of immigrants necessary to maintain a certain ratio of working-age adults to elderly people, and then calculate the number of new immigrants necessary to maintain this same ratio for the prior group of immigrants after *they* have become elderly and need caregivers, and so on, we are lost. The numbers only become astronomically larger and larger. The lesson is that mass ageing is a social and political issue that cannot be solved with math alone. Immigration reform would have to be one component of a broad transformation of wealth creation and distribution, how we spend our time, kinship structures and living arrangements, etc.
12 On the connection between nativism and environmentalism, see Daniel Denvir, *All-American Nativism: How the War on Immigrants Explains Politics as We Know It* (New York: Verso, 2020), 17–68.
13 I have chosen not to provide a citation of the killer's manifesto. While I think it is important to confront his ideas, I want to minimize my role in their circulation.
14 Ayal Feinberg, Regina Branton, and Valerie Martinez-Ebers, "Counties that Hosted a 2016 Trump Rally Saw a 226 Percent Increase in Hate Crimes," *The Washington Post*, March 22, 2019, www.washingtonpost.com/politics/2019/03/22/trumps-rhetoric-does-inspire-more-hate-crimes/.
15 Michael Edison Hayden, "Stephen Miller's Affinity for White Nationalism Revealed in Leaked Emails," *Hatewatch*, Southern Poverty Law Center, November 12, 2019, www.splcenter.org/hatewatch/2019/11/12/stephen-millers-affinity-white-nationalism-revealed-leaked-emails.
16 Boris and Klein, *Caring for America*, 224.

11 Watson, Champion of *White Jeopardy!*

When Ken Jennings was invited to compete on *Jeopardy!* against IBM's question-answering computer Watson, he felt like a time traveler. "People playing computers on game shows was the kind of thing I always imagined would happen in the future," Jennings recalled after being trounced by Watson over the course of three highly publicized *Jeopardy!* episodes in February 2011. Having previewed the coming AI dystopia, Jennings came back to the present to warn about the future of work and intelligence. In a 2013 TED Talk, Jennings presented himself as the first "worker" to be made technologically unemployable by the latest automation: "I felt like quiz show contestant was now the first job that had become obsolete under this new regime of thinking computers. And it hasn't been the last." But while Jennings claimed to be the contemporary equivalent of the factory worker who had been replaced by an older generation of industrial robots, he also suggested that his defeat was far more significant. For if Watson could beat a self-styled "know-it-all," then surely "cultural literacy," "cultural heritage," and even "civilization" was at stake. Jennings implored his audience to cherish "curious, inquisitive people who like to learn"—in other words, people like himself—and to resist the temptation to delegate thinking and cultural memory to computers.[1]

Jennings's postgame commentary was a remarkable display of narcissism by a trivia show contestant whose few seconds of fame were over. Yet when Jennings puffed himself up into a paragon of knowledge and culture, he spoke from the very subject position that *Jeopardy!* had created for him and that IBM needed to signify Watson's achievement of "intelligence." Alongside DeepMind's AlphaGo, Watson has been the most visible and widely discussed example of AI's new cognitive powers. For Brynjolfsson and McAfee, Watson proves that "our digital machines have escaped their narrow confines and started to demonstrate broad abilities in pattern recognition, complex communication, and other domains that used to be exclusively human."[2] But let us imagine an alternate history in which Watson's 2011 victory was not against Jennings and co-contestant Brad Rutter, two white men, but against a working-class, lesbian woman of color. Since the woman would not count as a figure of universal knowledge in hegemonic US culture, this hypothetical victory on *Jeopardy!* would have been just that: a victory on a popular TV show. To rise from the particular to the universal, to turn a game show into a staging ground for the rise of the robots, to transform the specific skills (and luck) needed to win on *Jeopardy!* into symbols of intelligence tout court, IBM required more than processing power and new algorithms. The corporation needed the cultural authority of white male nerdiness.

According to one origin story, Watson was born during Jennings's 74-game winning streak in 2004. An IBM manager observed how the dinner crowd at a restaurant stopped eating to watch Jennings on a TV set in the bar. Whereas *Jeopardy!* had previously limited winners to five consecutive appearances, a rule change enabled a polite, blandly humorous software engineer to become a popular repeat "character" on the show. Like any good prophet of automation, the IBM manager saw a person performing well and wondered how a machine could do better. Perhaps Jennings could be the next Garry Kasparov? After the company's Deep Blue computer had beaten the legendary chess master in 1997, executives were looking to strengthen the IBM brand through another public event. Google had search, Microsoft had software, Apple had the Mac and iPhone, so IBM would concentrate on consulting. Global Services was its biggest division, and by 2009 60% of the company's revenues would come from services.[3] If IBM could create a computer to analyze vast databases and quickly and accurately answer natural-language questions on *Jeopardy!*, it could not only create a compelling cultural narrative of its computing expertise but also orient future expectations toward new products. *Jeopardy!* would thus become the arena for a massively expensive advertisement for IBM's latest AI services. For all its significance as a breakthrough in natural language processing, the version of Watson that won on *Jeopardy!* was an elaborate prop for subsequent products like Watson Natural Language Understanding, Supply Chain Insights with Watson, and especially Watson Health, IBM's flagship Watson service.[4]

Initially, some IBM researchers were skeptical that a *Jeopardy!*-playing computer was a valid scientific achievement. They immediately recognized that Watson was a "publicity stunt."[5] What was at issue for IBM, however, was not an objective measure of science but its cultural signification. Deep Blue's defeat of Kasparov was no more or less inherently scientific than Watson's victory over Jennings and Rutter.[6] The difference is that in the earlier contest, IBM used the cultural prestige of chess and chess masters as a yardstick for Deep Blue's abilities, whereas Watson signaled that IBM recognized the game show and mass culture as the terrain for constructing future expectations. At the center of both matches was not intelligence itself, which does not exist in the singular or outside of context, but a corporate brand's appeal to particular *representations* of intelligence. Paul Horn, head of IBM Research, explained that the company chose *Jeopardy!* because "people associated it with intelligence."[7] Horn's statement illustrates that dominant discourses of AI are cultural *all the way down* because they mobilize "associations" or metonymies of human intelligence whenever they claim to replicate or supersede it. And such associations reflect the unequal distribution of cultural power—the power to "make things mean."[8] By collaborating with *Jeopardy!*, IBM capitalized on a powerful mass-cultural apparatus that registers and helps to reproduce what "intelligence" means.

   Jeopardy!, which first aired in 1964, is a child of the quiz show scandals of the late 1950s. In an attempt to rebrand, TV networks remade the quiz show into the *game* show. The latter pivoted away from the quiz shows' elite knowledges and large cash prizes and added more elements of play and luck.[9] Accordingly, *Jeopardy!* includes elements of gambling in the Daily Double and mixes highbrow and popular culture in its questions.[10] Although today's contestants can again win large monetary prizes, they are presented not as elites but as ordinary people "like us." During his winning streak Jennings emphasized that he was just a "regular person who is as weirded out by all of this as anybody else who's watching the game."[11] *New York Times* TV critic Alessandra Stanley contrasted Jennings to reality show contestants who "vie over who can eat more cockroaches" and lauded him as "a throwback to the days when ordinary people got on television for doing well, not something shameless."[12] But what distinguishes *Jeopardy!* in the US cultural field is that it synthesizes contestants' pseudo-democratic ordinariness with the quiz show's intellectual prestige. *The Washington Post* wouldn't have called Jennings "the brainiest man in TV game show history" if he had been a champion on other post-scandal shows like *Wheel of Fortune, The Price is Right,* or *Family Feud.*[13]

   Growing up, I never liked *Jeopardy!* because it made me feel stupid. I later realized that I had felt this way not simply because I could grasp only the easiest pop-cultural references but because the *kind* of knowledge that the show celebrated was generally not the kind of knowledge that people in my working-class Chicanx family possessed. In his chapter on the quiz show in *Television Culture* (1987), John Fiske argues that shows like *Jeopardy!* rehearse and naturalize the ideologies of capitalist education:

> all students (supposedly) start equal: those with natural ability pass successively more discriminating tests (examinations) and emerge as the highly qualified few who are fitted (by nature, so the story goes) for the high-income jobs, and positions with high degrees of social power and influence.[14]

Similarly, the *Jeopardy!* contestant crops up on stage as if randomly selected from all "ordinary people," proves his—the winners are predominantly men—"natural" intelligence by answering exam-like questions, and earns money and recognition meritocratically. What I vaguely sensed as a boy and young man was that this ritual was not about me or people like me: it was largely a celebration of middle-class and professional white men and their command of facts. Fiske observes that the sort of knowledge that predominates on *Jeopardy!*, "the 'factual,' 'academic' type," is "most closely connected with the notion of power and cultural capital. [...] This knowledge has an empirical base whose 'facticity' masks its origin in, and maintenance of, a system of social power."[15] To be a master of facts is to embody objectivity and a privileged position in the social hierarchy that appears to be equally objective and factual.

By way of contrast, *Family Feud* reveals why *Jeopardy!* was ideally suited for IBM's purposes. *Family Feud* centers a social unit, the family, and asks the family to intuit how other people have responded to an opinion survey. *Family Feud* thus privileges knowledges that are "not gained through school or reading, but rather through common social experience and interaction." Since these knowledges are social, not factual, they afford "no absolute right and wrong answers and thus cannot be possessed or guarded by an elite." The winning family is the one who "can predict the social norms, who knows best what most people are thinking."[16] While *Jeopardy!* symbolically recreates the process by which schools examine and accredit the "best and brightest," success on *Family Feud* requires no academic credentials. *Family Feud* presents knowledge as common social experience distributed across the family as a microcosm of the social world; one study even claims that generationally and racially diverse families do best on the show because they collectively have broad social knowledge.[17] In contrast, *Jeopardy!* presents knowledge as decontextualized facts residing in the brain of an individual "genius" who is usually an educated white male with a middle-class or professional background.[18] Of course Jennings was the personification of "intelligence" in the eyes of IBM executives, engineers, and business sf writers: he is their mirror image.

In his book *Brainiac: Adventures in the Curious, Competitive, Compulsive World of Trivia Buffs* (2006), Jennings addresses some of the gender and racial inequalities of *Jeopardy!* only to disavow them. According to one analysis of the fan-created *J! Archive*, women have made up about 40% of contestants and have won only 30% of the games played since the show was rebooted in 1984.[19] The *Jeopardy!* Hall of Fame, which tracks the all-time top ten contestants in terms of prize money and winning streaks, is dominated by educated white men. No women of color are listed; perhaps even more structurally absent are members of the working class of any gender or race.[20] Yet when Jennings recounts his initial *Jeopardy!* audition, he ignores preexisting structural inequalities and assures the reader that the audition room is a space of American freedom in which black women have the same opportunities that he has:

> I crane my neck curiously to look at the demographic of the room. There are plenty of the middle-aged white guys who make up *Jeopardy!*'s core contestant population, but on the whole, the room looks like America. I'm sitting in front of [an] African American woman [...] , and she's representative of a pretty good smattering of women and minorities.[21]

Jennings is so aware of gender and race that he cranes his neck to document them. The single black woman and the "smattering of women and minorities" for which she is a token are enough to reassure him that he is competing on a level playing field—a conclusion that presumes that women and people of color are just a "smattering" of America, sufficiently represented by a few stand-ins, while "middle-aged white guys" are the core.

When a female contestant tells Jennings that not only the selection process but the show's questions are biased because the writers are also mostly "middle-aged white guys," Jennings's retort is typical of the guardian of facts: "the knowledge they [the questions] test is just simple factual recall about the world we all live in, men or women."[22] Ironically, researchers have shown that the very neutrality that Jennings defends is gendered. Sheila Brownlow, Rebecca Whitener, and Janet M. Rupert claim that the *domains* in which Jennings's "simple factual recall" occurs can be categorized according to whether they reflect the kinds of knowledge and interests that men and women are socially expected to have. Female *Jeopardy!* contestants are more likely to choose gender-neutral domains than men; if there is something like sheer facticity on *Jeopardy!*, women are more likely to perform it because they have been socialized to lack confidence in their knowledge in male domains, are weary of appearing unlikeable if they outperform men in these domains, have lower expectations of their abilities, and are more likely to attribute their success to sheer luck.[23] Jennings can imagine that his knowledge is neutral only because his own identity as an educated white male has become a transparent lens onto the world, enabling him to misperceive the particular things that interest him as sheer facts, equally available to all. When Watson beat Jennings and Rutter, the system simply bested the white male "brainiac" at his own game. According to my rough estimate, the match's questions and answers referenced only two people who were not males of European descent: Martin Luther King, Jr. and the rapper 50 Cent.[24]

I would love to see Jennings and Watson on a real-life version of the *Saturday Night Live* skit "Black Jeopardy." The brilliance of "Black Jeopardy" is that it puts the otherwise transparent white subject position *on the board* as a category, "White People." By centering black vernacular knowledges that are excluded from hegemonic significations of intelligence—including knowledge of whites *as* whites—"Black Jeopardy" turns the universalized white subject into a minority and foregrounds the social particularity of *all* claims to intelligence as such. The skit reveals that a word is missing from its counterpart's title: *White Jeopardy!* For what masquerades on the show as "human knowledge" reflects the greater power of a particular segment of humanity to make things mean.

No sooner did Watson win on *Jeopardy!* than IBM announced several partnerships with the health care industry. The game show champion would become Dr. Watson, a natural language tool that analyzes vast stores of medical data and makes recommendations. In a humorous 2016 TV ad in which a human psychologist and Watson council neurotic robots against world domination, IBM assures viewers that its new AI services will not displace us: "IBM Watson works *with* humans." But the philosophical thematic of "human vs. machine" is a red herring. To teach Watson to play *Jeopardy!*, IBM trained the computer on databases like *J!* Archive and Wikipedia; in other words, the company appropriated the products of human labor and made them appear to be the inherent properties of a computer. Medical data is not only more strictly controlled than online user-generated data but also unstructured. Doctors' notes, for example, continue to baffle Watson. The numerous health care collaborations and projects that IBM has announced since 2011 have yielded few commercial products, and IBM's own internal records reveal that customers have complained about Watson for Oncology's inaccurate recommendations for cancer treatment. IBM's three-year collaboration with the University of Texas's MD Anderson Cancer Center was a debacle that ended with a canceled contract, no functional tool, and a $62 million bill.[25]

Watson tells us nothing about the "human." It does not "demonstrate computers' newfound power to replicate *our* cognitive skills," as business sf writer Nicholas Carr claims.[26] When automation is designed to replace and control manual and service labor—the factory worker, the warehouse picker, the taxi driver, the housewife, the care worker—its ideal is the technologized slave, but when automation represents "intelligence," it assumes the alleged objectivity and neutrality of the white male mind. Watson was named after a white businessman, IBM CEO Thomas J. Watson; it was designed by a team of predominantly white male corporate technologists; it outperformed two white men in a mass-cultural event that is generally dominated by middle- and upper-class white men. Jennings's narcissism was the parting shot of a white intelligence upon which IBM had modeled Watson, and that the computer appeared to appropriate for itself. But Jennings's narcissism ultimately pales in comparison with the narcissism behind the automation myth of Watson—the third age of automation's greatest monument to the genius of credentialed whiteness.

Notes

1 Ken Jennings, "Watson, Jeopardy and Me, the Obsolete Know-it-all," *TED*, February 2013, www.ted.com/talks/ken_jennings_watson_jeopardy_and_me_t he_obsolete_know_it_all/transcript.
2 Brynjolfsson and McAfee, *The Second Machine Age*, 91.
3 Stephen Baker, *Final Jeopardy: Man vs. Machine and the Quest to Know Everything* (Boston, MA: Houghton Mifflin Harcourt, 2011), 24. My account of the genesis of Watson draws on Baker.
4 See the IBM website for an overview of Watson-based AI services: www.ibm .com/us-en/products/categories?technologyTopics[0][0]=cat.topic:Cognitive ComputingAndAI&from_page=landing.
5 Baker, *Final Jeopardy*, 22.
6 "[C]hess is not a test of intelligence; it is the test of a particular skill—the skill of playing chess. [...] [T]hinking chess was a test of intelligence was based on a false cultural premise that brilliant chess players were brilliant minds, more gifted than those around them. Yes, many intelligent people excel at chess, but chess, or any other single skill, does not denote intelligence." George V. Neville-Neill, "The Chess Player Who Couldn't Pass the Salt," *Communications of the ACM [Association for Computing Machinery]* 60, no. 4, December 26, 2016, https://queue.acm.org/detail.cfm?id=3029797.
7 Baker, *Final Jeopardy*, 7.
8 Stuart Hall, "The Work of Representation," in *Representation: Cultural Representations and Signifying Practices*, ed. Stuart Hall (London: Sage, 1997), 24.
9 Olaf Hoerschelmann, *Rules of the Game: Quiz Shows and American Culture* (Albany, NY: State University of New York Press, 2006), chap. 4.
10 To be more precise, *Jeopardy!* contestants are provided answers for which they must supply the correct questions. Popular accounts of the show's history often mention that this inversion of the standard question-answer format was a tongue-in-cheek way to distinguish *Jeopardy!* from the old quiz shows.
11 Elaine Aradillas, "Savoring a Little Attention to Go with the Big Bucks," *The New York Times*, July 13, 2004, www.nytimes.com/2004/07/13/arts/savoring-a-li ttle-attention-to-go-with-the-big-bucks.html.
12 Alessandra Stanley, "O.K., Alex, Smart Nerds For $1 Million," *The New York Times*, July 13, 2004, www.nytimes.com/2004/07/13/arts/the-tv-watch-ok-alex -smart-nerds-for-1-million.html.
13 Lisa de Moraes, "This Game Show Contestant Is in 'Jeopardy!'" *Washington Post*, November 30, 2004, www.washingtonpost.com/wp-dyn/articles/A21948 -2004Nov30.html.
14 John Fiske, *Television Culture*, 2nd ed. (New York: Routledge, 2010), 268.
15 Fiske, *Television Culture*, 269.
16 Fiske, *Television Culture*, 270.
17 Gabriella A. Bucci, and Rafael Tenorio, "Group Diversity and Salience: A Natural Experiment from a Television Game Show," *Journal of Socio-Economics* 39, no. 2 (2010): 306–15.

18   Since 2010 *Family Feud* has been hosted by African American comedian Steve Harvey and features black families so regularly that it has inspired the ridiculous but predictable charge of "reverse racism" against whites. See reviews of the show on the Internet Movie Database at www.imdb.com/title/tt0177440/reviews. For a compelling explanation of why a black comedian will never host *Jeopardy!* see Ann duCille, *Technicolored: Reflections on Race in the Time of TV* (Durham, NC: Duke University Press, 2018), 41. See also duCille's critique of Harvey's sexualized buffoonery.

19   Ben Blatt, and Amanda Hess, "Do Men Wager More than Women in *Jeopardy?* A *Slate* Investigation," *Slate*, March 5, 2014, https://slate.com/human-interest/20 14/03/gender-differences-in-jeopardy-alex-trebek-says-women-wager-less-in-d aily-double-bets.html.

20   The Hall of Fame can be viewed at www.jeopardy.com/contestant-zone/hall-of -fame.

21   Jennings, *Brainiac*, 20.

22   Jennings, 128.

23   Sheila Brownlow, Rebecca Whitener, and Janet M. Rupert, "'I'll Take Gender Differences for $1000!' Domain-Specific Intellectual Success on 'Jeopardy,'" *Sex Roles* 38, no. 3/4 (1998): 269–85. A related study of *Who Wants to Be a Millionaire* is also suggestive of how socialization affects women before they can get on a game show in the first place: women are particularly vulnerable to social expectations and thus avoid risking public judgement and embarrassment. Judith E. Larkin, and Harvey A. Pines, "Gender and Risk in Public Performance," *Sex Roles* 49, no. 5/6 (2003): 197–210.

24   The entire match is documented on *J!* Archive: www.j-archive.com/showgame .php?game_id=3575; http://www.j-archive.com/showgame.php?game_id=3576 ; www.j-archive.com/showgame.php?game_id=3577. *Salon*'s Deborah Sosin informally studied 18 episodes in 2013 and found that men were the answer to nearly 80% of questions for which both men and women could be answers. Deborah Sosin, "'What is Sexism, Alex': Close the 'Jeopardy' Gender Gap!" *Salon*, September 29, 2013, www.salon.com/2013/09/29/what_is_sexism_alex_ close_the_jeopardy_gender_gap/.

25   Casey Ross, "IBM's Watson Supercomputer Recommended 'Unsafe and Incorrect' Cancer Treatments, Internal Documents Show," *STAT*, July 25, 2018, www.statnews.com/2018/07/25/ibm-watson-recommended-unsafe-in correct-treatments/; Eliza Strickland, "How IBM Watson Overpromised and Underdelivered on AI Health Care," *IEEE Spectrum*, April 2, 2019, https://sp ectrum.ieee.org/biomedical/diagnostics/how-ibm-watson-overpromised-and -underdelivered-on-ai-health-care.

26   Carr, *The Glass Cage*, 120, my emphasis.

Conclusion
Reification and Utopia in Automation

In the closing pages of *Mythologies*, Barthes turns his analysis on himself and concludes that the "mythologist"—the critic of myth, not its producer—can relate only negatively to the mythical object he seeks to denaturalize. The mythologist is alienated from the object's real substratum, its material as opposed to its mythological existence, as well as from the object's alternative possibilities. Looking back on his treatment of the myths surrounding the child poet Minou Drouet, Barthes admits that he "had to ignore, in her, under the enormous myth with which she is cumbered, something like a tender, open possibility." This same ignorance blocks the mythologist's access to a future beyond the currently hegemonic myths: "It is forbidden for him to imagine what the rest of the world will concretely be like when the immediate object of his criticism has disappeared. Utopia is an impossible luxury for him."[1] At best, the mythologist can recognize that the inadequacy of a sheerly negative attitude is not a personal fault but a condition of living in a mythological social world.

Echoing Barthes's parting gesture, I want to end this book by asking: is there a "tender, open possibility" in automation myths that my technoclastic treatment of business sf has overlooked? Have I, like Barthes, locked myself out of utopia? Barthes was right that the impasses of thinking reflect the social world's contradictions, but I am not persuaded by his treatment of utopian speculation as an "impossible luxury." One task remains: to think about myths more *dialectically* than I have thus far. This does not mean simply to toggle from a negative critique of their "bad" side to an affirmative appreciation of their "good" side, but rather to capture the movement of the good *in* the bad and vice versa. For this purpose, Fredric Jameson's essay "Reification and Utopia in Mass Culture" serves as a useful supplement to *Mythologies*.

Jameson's essay breaks the horns of the dilemma between a concept of popular culture that celebrates its authentic expression of common tastes and a concept of mass culture that critiques the capitalist culture industry and its ideological manipulation of consumers. Jameson's key insight is that culture cannot be ideological without being utopian. For example, *The Godfather* (1972) invites the viewer to substitute the crimes of the Corleone family mafia for American big business, thereby redirecting criticism of capitalism toward organized crime. Capitalist business, ruthless in its own right, is implicitly coded as normal, whereas crime is represented as a violent exception and deviation. But the very unit of *The Godfather*'s reification of capitalism, the Corleone family, is also utopian. The Old World family is a figure of the love, belonging, and order from which the middle-class white American feels alienated:

> the ethnic group can seem to project an image of social reintegration by way of the patriarchal and authoritarian family of the past. Thus the tightly knit bonds of the Mafia family [...], the protective security of the (god-)father with his omnipresent authority, offers a contemporary pretext for a Utopian fantasy.[2]

In other words, while a critique of *The Godfather* that focuses only on its reification of capitalism is insufficient, it is equally inadequate to tack on a reading of its utopian elements. The film channels utopian longing for social reintegration and solidarity *by* diverting attention from business; it shunts away a critique of capitalism *by* offering viewers the ethnic, patriarchal family in its stead. Reification and utopia are sticky. Rotate them slightly and their apparent opposition turns into magnetic attraction.

Jameson has trained his dialectical method not only on popular films but also, and more infamously, on the mammoth American retailer Walmart. Whereas many a utopian thinker is probably willing to grant that a Hollywood film contains utopian traces, a monopolistic, price-slashing, ruthlessly anti-union and anti-worker corporation is a far more counterintuitive example. This is precisely the point for Jameson. He is less interested in predicting that Walmart will become postcapitalist, or in spelling out an economic and political program to make it so, than in practicing utopian speculation on an institution that fully embodies the capitalist present and its apparent grip on the future.[3] Walmart is an occasion for Jameson to perform a style of dialectical imagination that locates the positive in the deepest recesses of the negative—not in order to advance a plan for further developing the positive but for the sake of "reawakening [...] the imagination of possible and alternate futures, a reawakening of that historicity which our system—offering itself as the very end of history—necessarily represses and paralyzes." If the dialectical reading of mass culture is *symptomatic*—it detects utopian longing in unexpected places—then the dialectical reading of Walmart is *anamnestic*, a dis-forgetting of historical possibility, a revivification of "long dormant parts of the mind, unused organs of political and historical and social imagination which have virtually atrophied for lack of use."[4]

The symptomatic and anamnestic elements of Jameson's dialectic help the critic of automation recognize the utopian impulse in the enchanted objects of automation myth. A symptomatic reading of Baxter and Amazon robots acknowledges that the mythological haze surrounding them is made all the denser by Americans' dissatisfaction with the repetitive, boring, and physically and psychologically damaging wage labor that robots are supposed to overtake. The fictional disappearance of workers from factories and warehouses is tightly wound around workers' real hope for freedom from drudgery and "bullshit jobs." In *Automation and Utopia* (2019), John Danaher makes a strong case for thinking that wage labor is *structurally* bad: employers have too much power over workers, jobs are increasingly Taylorized and precarious, wages are unjustly distributed, and the working day colonizes our time and energy. Many people are unhappy at their jobs but recognize that work's structural badness is extremely difficult to change. When automation mythologists promise that robots will free workers, they tap into the lived reality at the heart of Danaher's position: you *should* hate your job.[5]

Moreover, anyone who has endured the purgatory of Los Angeles gridlock or lost a loved one in a car accident can see the rational kernel in the mystical shell of the self-driving car. Like the Brothers Grimm fairytale of the magic table that sets itself with food and drink (*"Tischlein, deck dich!"*), the smart home appeals to the desires of the tired and weary, the harried mothers who wish that a few spoken words could automatically take care of dinner. Louise Aronson's hypothesis that a robot caregiver could make her patient smile more often and ease her loneliness is grounded in the doctor's concern for the wellbeing of the elderly, and I share her hope that life can last longer for many more people and still be *worth* living. The white corporate dreams of Dr. Watson are symptomatic of the massive dysfunctionality of the US healthcare system.

Thus, I want to stress that the myths that I have tried to denaturalize in this book are not "wrong" in some totalizing and moralistic sense. On the contrary, business sf is one of the most powerful utopian discourses of our time. This is why business sf is worthy of sustained demystification and not a mere scam to be ignored. As another critic of automation discourse, Aaron Benanav, notes, "in a world reeling from the 'perfect storm' of climate change, rising inequality, recalcitrant neoliberalism and resurgent ethnonationalism, the automation theorists are the ones pushing through the catastrophe with a vision of an emancipated future."[6] To concede this point is to dis-forget the utopian energies coursing through the present—to remember that the present is *not* the best of all possible worlds, not even in the eyes of some if its greatest defenders.

But what happens to Jameson's dialectic when the utopian is no longer shouting in the wilderness? Jameson's position presupposes that utopian symptoms must be identified because capitalism appears immutable, and that the anamnestic "turning back" (ana-) of memory is necessary because of a pervasive not-remembering (a-mnesia). Although these suppositions remain generally valid, the Great Recession of 2008 weakened them to such a degree that anyone speculating about automation today is joined by a chorus of voices. The "unused organs" of imagination are being exercised anew. Not satisfied with detecting symptoms or performing utopian remembrance, automation futurists are extrapolating technosocial tendencies, dislodging them from countervailing forces in the present, imagining their full development, and sketching programs to realize or avoid these futures. If the dialectic finds the good in the bad, this type of speculation wants to pry them apart and make them stand separately before the imagination's tribunal.

We can broadly distinguish between two formations. This book has argued that utopian and dystopian business sf is a deterministic discourse that fetishizes innovation and fails to reckon fully with capitalism's systemic crises and its histories of class, gender, and racial domination. To put my critique of business sf dialectically, business sf's utopian traces are enmeshed in its failures and its failures are the condition of possibility of its utopianism. Such is the unresolvable contradiction of a mode of speculation that extols radical technosocial change in order to educate desire for a future that preserves capitalist social property relations and modes of production and reproduction—a future without substantive change, i.e., a ruse. In contrast, socialist and communist speculation draws on a powerful science fiction in classical Marxism: capitalist development of technology will eventually come into conflict with capitalist social relations that impede the material possibility of a world without scarcity, without wage labor, and without capitalism. Building an alternative to capitalism thus requires a political project that liberates already existing postcapitalist technological tendencies from their capitalist fetters.[7]

Much leftist utopian speculation about automation orbits around these ideas, but their most full-throated articulation is Aaron Bastani's *Fully Automated Luxury Communism*. Combining business sf's stage theories and Silicon Valley rhetoric, Bastani distinguishes among three technological Disruptions: the agricultural revolution, the industrial revolution, and the ongoing digital revolution. In the Third Disruption, "machines will be capable of replicating ever more of what was, until now, uniquely human work."[8] The result will be a crisis of technological unemployment that compounds the problems of climate change, resource scarcity, and the greying world population. Fully Automated Luxury Communism (FALC) is Bastani's political alternative. By unshackling technology from capitalism's profit imperative, labor market, and need for continual growth, a future communist society will use the technologies of the Third Disruption to produce universal material abundance. Powered by unlimited solar energy and built with minerals mined from outer space, automation will abolish work that is done to satisfy basic needs, thus transforming work into a free act of self-enrichment that is indistinguishable from leisure and play. Gene editing will solve the dilemmas of societal aging, while synthetic foods will put an end to environmentally destructive meat consumption. In contrast to the austere communist totalitarianisms of the past, Bastani's fully automated communist future possesses immense "collective wealth" and "all essential wants as well as creative desires are satisfied." "Communism is luxurious," Bastani continues, as if rebuking Barthes's remark on the luxury of utopia, "or it isn't communism."[9]

Fully Automated Luxury Communism is *The Second Machine Age* for Marxists. This is the book's greatest strength and weakness. On the one hand, while Brynjolfsson and McAfee finesse the political consequences of automation, Bastani is refreshingly clear that automation is a political project that raises fundamental questions about the social organization of labor, wealth, and power. He recognizes that automation is more than a neutral instrument; its uses and meanings are conditioned by social property relations and can thus take different paths in different hegemonic formations. Paul Mason's *Postcapitalism*, Nick Srnicek and Alex Williams's *Inventing the Future*, and Peter Frase's *Four Futures* are also solid on these points. Against business sf's founding assumption of the deterministic coevolution of capitalism and innovation, Bastani reminds us that, in Andrew Feenberg's terms, "no technological imperatives dictate the current social hierarchy" because "technology is a site of social struggle."[10] *Fully Automated Luxury Communism* is a forceful act of utopian dreaming because it unbundles technology's possibilities from capitalism and invites us into a prosperous and verdant future after the end of bullshit jobs. In the midst of the climate crisis, Bastani is right to insist that we *can* have nice things, and that the flourishing of the planet and non-human life need not come at the expense of human flourishing, especially for those humans who have hardly had a chance to flourish at all.

On the other hand, FALC is a castle made of business sf sand. Although his conclusions on the politics of automation are substantively different from those of Brynjolfsson and McAfee, Ford, and Kaplan, Bastani reaches these conclusions with the help of the same automation myths. When it comes to representing automation's enchanted objects, much of *Fully Automated Luxury Communism* is virtually indistinguishable from *The Second Machine Age*, *Rise of the Robots*, and *Humans Need Not Apply*. There is the same capitalist-Hegelian triad of agriculture, industry, and digitization; the same faith in ever-accelerating capitalist technological dynamism; the same naturalization of Moore's Law; the same expectations that entrepreneurs and startups will eventually perfect their technologies; the same fauxtomatic assumptions about the capacities of self-driving cars and Watson; the same tech advertising disguised in the indicative. Summarizing Marx's view of the industrial revolution, Bastani writes that "technology transformed work, and could improve people's lives, but only if it was coupled with an appropriate politics."[11] Here we see business sf's technological determinism in Marxist trappings. For Bastani's Marxism is business sf plus Marxist politics—where "politics" is essentially a set of values and policies that react to semi-autonomous forces in the technological domain. FALC's de-automation of politics and its automation of technical automation are joined at the hip.

It would be easy at this point to rehearse platitudes about the impossibility of imagining the future and the inevitability with which speculation reinscribes actuality. After all, we are immersed in the world like fish in water, and while some of us may learn to leap above the waterline, even a flying fish has no real sense of the not-water world. Capitalism is our frame of reference; the most imaginative utopian thinking can only negate it or recombine its elements. But this is not my view. I do not believe in a principled refusal to imagine utopia, nor do I wish to settle into the banal comforts of aporia. Imagining detailed, systemic alternatives to capitalism is not only valid but imperative to counteract business sf and help to convince people that other technosocial relations are plausible. If capitalism's critics cannot provide a compelling case for an alternative, then they also cannot expect political actors to take the risks and make the commitments that would be necessary to bring it about. Describing how to reinvigorate the socialist alternative, Sam Gindin observes that "winning people over to a complex protracted struggle to introduce profoundly new ways of producing, living, and relating to each other demands a much deeper engagement with socialism's *actual possibility*." It is not enough to critique capitalism and focus on "getting to" an alternative, for "it is now at least as important to convince prospective socialists that there really is a 'there' to get to."[12]

Although a concrete elaboration of an alternative is beyond the scope of this book, I do hope that *Against Automation Mythologies* can make a small contribution to this project by clarifying its starting points. Instead of taking the full automation of labor as a first principle and then imagining an appropriate politics, utopian speculation should extrapolate from the ruse of the robots. The problem with taking full automation as a first principle is that it allows the utopian dreamer to assume that new social relations of production and reproduction will appear with all the self-acting and self-regulating momentum of a robot. The more complete the automation, the more likely the speculation "solves" the problem of new relations of production and reproduction by imagining them out of existence (at least for humans). Yet these relations, including their histories of domination, are precisely what demand conscious reimagining and remaking. Full automation does not tell us how to dream a free, democratic, equitable, and environmentally sustainable organization of technosocial labor; it makes it easier to ignore the very need for this dream.

Take the question of scarcity. In FALC, there is "a limitless, virtually free supply of anything."[13] This abundance encompasses not only necessities but even, appropriately, whiskey, which Bastani predicts will become an "informational good" and "technically subject to infinite replication."[14] But as much as I like the idea of universal whiskey, whether a good or service should be produced and reproduced depends not on sheer technical feasibility but on a historically evolving web of social relations that connect needs and desires to labor and nature. Capitalism weaves this web through the mechanisms of market domination. Even if we accept Bastani's questionable assumptions that these same mechanisms will push synthetic food startups to perfect their technologies, and that these technologies can be easily appropriated for communism, we can still ask how future communists who own the means of production will decide if using water, malt, and labor—at the very least, the labor of designing and maintaining the replicating machines—to make whiskey is more important than using the same resources and time for something else. As soon as there is a conflict between one ensemble of needs, desires, resources, time, and labor and another ensemble, there is scarcity as well as the necessity of democratic political forms and practices to deal with it equitably.[15] Automation is one possible solution, but so is sharing and rotating labor among people.[16] In this sense, scarcity is negotiable but still constitutive of any cooperative human endeavor. Post-scarcity is utopian when it helps to liberate the imagination from austerity, but it is reification when it serves as an excuse to pretend that automation will eliminate complex *choices* about how to negotiate competing needs and desires and claims on labor and nature, effectively removing questions of production and reproduction from the domain of political deliberation.

Maybe the robots will rise one day; maybe not. Given the future's unknowability, I propose that instead of echoing business sf's premise— "What if automation continues?"—leftist speculation's starting points should be *lateral* moves that sidestep automation myths and reframe the basic terms of social dreaming. What if dexterous robots or self-driving cars or smart homes can never be perfected, at least not in ways that match their advertising? What if the trajectory of these technologies is not mass leisure or unemployment but old domination in new guises? What if, instead of repeating the master's stories about his tools, we went on strike against the speculation that the "end of work" will happen *to* the people whose labor sustains society? What if the material conditions for postcapitalism are not technical but political? What if critical utopians extrapolated not from capitalism's ruthless pursuit of productive efficiency but from the struggles and political visions of working-class, anti-racist, feminist, and environmental movements? What if, instead of speculating about the techno-republican perfection of servitude, the task of utopian imagination was to prefigure emancipatory political subjectivity and organization, which would then serve as the basis for collective deliberation about if, when, and how to automate? For these ends, there is more futurity in a single strike by homecare or warehouse workers than in the most gee-whiz news report on the latest Silicon Valley "disruption."

Setting out from lateral coordinates also helps the utopian dreamer to pivot away from the assumption that alienated technology can disalienate labor. David Noble once proposed a deceptively simple thought experiment: imagine that an engineer designs a robot for a colleague. When the engineer gives the robot to his colleague on her birthday, he tells her: "I have built for you my finest machine; it is so well designed, it can be run by an idiot."[17] Obviously the friend will be offended by the implication that she is an idiot. Yet the assumption that automation should simplify and deskill a work process so that only "idiotic" supplemental labor is required—think of Amazon pickers—is such a deeply entrenched design norm that most engineers and managers would hardly object to such a robot, as long as it were created for others and not for themselves. Indeed, for many managers seeking ways to cheapen and discipline labor, the idiocy required by a technology probably makes it more attractive. Noble's point is that

> it matters a great deal [...] whether or not the designers and users are the same people, whether or not they know each other, whether or not they view each other as equals, whether or not they have power over each other, whether or not they are friends.[18]

The technologies upon which business sf and leftist utopians base their extrapolations embody social relations of antagonism, not friendship; of hierarchy, not equality. By placing workers' struggles at the forefront of speculation, we can open up a very different set of questions: what if robots and other automated systems were designed not for idiots but for workers with valued skills and knowledges? What if the goal of automation were not just to eliminate work—although this is always a political option—but also to make work more interesting, even more *pleasurable*? Can we imagine something like a Baxter for the people—a collaborative robot, designed transparently with the direct input of users, that creatively challenges and amplifies human capacities?

Since technology will be essential to a future after capitalism, it is equally essential to continue to symptomatically and anamnestically examine the postcapitalist elements of today's technology. But perhaps speculation sees these elements only by moving laterally across extrapolation itself. Another technosociality is possible, but it may not be accessible to the utopian imagination on any timeline. Against Marx's famous claim that the new world slumbers in the womb of the old, utopia might be better understood as being as akin to this world as a photograph, created in a techno–human exchange, of a child who never was or will be born. The child in the photograph is happy, evoking longing for an existence neither behind nor ahead of us, neither nostalgic nor prognostic, only strangely different. And better.

Notes

1 Barthes, *Mythologies*, 272.
2 Fredric Jameson, *Signatures of the Visible* (New York: Routledge, 1992), 33.
3 For a more sustained elaboration of Jameson's idea, see Leigh Phillips, and Michal Rozworski, *The People's Republic of Walmart: How the World's Biggest Corporations Are Laying the Foundation for Socialism* (New York: Verso, 2019).
4 Fredric Jameson, *Valences of the Dialectic* (New York: Verso, 2009), 434.
5 John Danaher, *Automation and Utopia: Human Flourishing in a World Without Work* (Cambridge, MA: Harvard University Press, 2019), chap. 2. Danaher's book is a hybrid that lies somewhere between business sf for philosophers and leftist speculation without Marxism. Building on business sf's future expectations and post-work discourses, Danaher constructs a philosophically rigorous argument that full automation will allow people to reorganize social life around games. On the one hand, *Automation and Utopia* is a remarkable vision of how human life can flourish after the end of wage labor; on the other hand, it is another automation of automation.
6 Benanav, "Automation and the Future of Work—1," 14.
7 Steven Shaviro, *No Speed Limit: Three Essays on Accelerationism* (Minneapolis, MN: University of Minnesota Press, 2015), chap. 1, Kindle.
8 Bastani, *Fully Automated Luxury Communism*, 37.
9 Bastani, 56.
10 Feenberg, *Questioning Technology*, 83.
11 Bastani, *Fully Automated*, 62.
12 Sam Gindin, "Socialism for Realists," *Catalyst* 2, no. 3 (2018): 8, 9. My emphasis.
13 Bastani, *Fully Automated*, 137.
14 Bastani, 180.
15 Gindin, "Socialism for Realists," 14.
16 Benanav, "Automation and the Future of Work—2," 138.
17 Noble, *Forces of Production*, 44.
18 Noble, 45.

Index